Maths

The 11+ Practice Book

with Assessment Tests

For the CEM (Durham University) test

Ages
9-10

Practise • Prepare • Pass
Everything your child needs for 11+ success

How to use this Practice Book

This book is divided into two parts — themed question practice and full-length assessment tests. There are answers and detailed explanations in the pull-out section at the back of the book.

Themed question practice

- Each page contains practice questions divided by topic. Use these pages to work out your child's strengths and the areas they find tricky. The questions get harder down each page.

Assessment tests

- The second half of the book contains five full-length assessment tests, each with a mix of question types from the first half of the book. They take a similar form to the maths sections of the real test.

- You can print off multiple-choice answer sheets from our website, www.cgplearning.co.uk/11+, so your child can practise taking the tests as if they're sitting the real thing.

- If you want to give your child timed practice, give them a time limit of 29 minutes for each test, and ask them to work as quickly and carefully as they can.

- Your child should aim for a mark of around 85% (41 questions correct) in each test. If they score less than this, use their results to work out the areas they need more practice on.

- If they haven't managed to finish the test in time, they need to work on increasing their speed, whereas if they have made a lot of mistakes, they need to work more carefully.

- Keep track of your child's scores using the progress chart on the inside back cover of the book.

Published by CGP

Editors:
Joe Brazier, Rachel Grocott, Shaun Harrogate, Lucy Loveluck, Paul Jordin, Sophie Scott

Contributors:
John Davis, Cynthia Deeson, Sumyya Hassan, John Hawkins

With thanks to Rachael Rogers and Rachel Patterson for the proofreading.

Please note that CGP is not associated with CEM or The University of Durham in any way. This book does not include any official questions and it is not endorsed by CEM or The University of Durham.

CEM, Centre for Evaluation and Monitoring, Durham University and *The University of Durham* are all trademarks of The University of Durham.

ISBN: 978 1 84762 562 5
Website: www.cgpbooks.co.uk
Printed by Elanders Ltd, Newcastle upon Tyne
Clipart from CorelDRAW®

Based on the classic CGP style created by Richard Parsons.

Photocopying — it's dull, it takes ages... and sometimes it's a bit naughty. Luckily, it's dead cheap, easy and quick to order more copies of this book from CGP — just call us on 0870 750 1242. Phew!

Text, design, layout and original illustrations © Coordination Group Publications Ltd. (CGP) 2013
All rights reserved.

CONTENTS

Place Value

Circle the correct place value of the underlined digit for each question below.

1.	1**6**3.92	Hundreds	Units	Tens	Tenths
2.	**3**780.3	Thousands	Units	Thousandths	Hundredths
3.	298.0**39**	Tenths	Hundredths	Thousandths	Hundreds
4.	72 636.**4**8	Units	Tens	Tenths	Hundreds
5.	5591.28**1**	Thousands	Thousandths	Units	Tenths

Circle the smallest number in each row below.

6.	16.2	32.9	84.9	172.3	1.62
7.	32.4	30.2	302	3.02	32.0
8.	123.7	132.7	312.7	127.3	317.2
9.	1.35	1.27	1.61	1.84	1.37
10.	1.044	0.144	10.44	0.441	1.444

Hint: You need to look at the place value of the digits to work out which number is the smallest.

/ 10

The table below shows the results of the Class 5B 80 m race.

Name	Jake	Holly	Jack	Micah	Olivia
Time (seconds)	14.36	13.59	14.4	13.5	14.04

11. Circle the name of the person who came last in the race.

    A   Micah   **B**   Jack   **C**   Olivia   **D**   Jake

12. How long did it take the winner to complete the race?   ☐☐.☐☐ seconds

13. How long did the second slowest person take to complete the race?   ☐☐.☐☐ seconds

14. Whose time is marked on this number line?

14   15

    A   Jake's   **B**   Jack's   **C**   Holly's   **D**   Micah's

15. Whose time is marked on this number line?

13   14

    A   Holly's   **B**   Olivia's   **C**   Micah's   **D**   Jack's

/ 5

Rounding Up and Down

Round the following numbers.

1. 786 to the nearest 10

2. 851 to the nearest 100

3. 279 to the nearest 100

4. 8578 to the nearest 1000

5. 4426 to the nearest 1000

6. 2421 to the nearest 100

7. 27 642 people live in Graston.
How many people is this to the nearest 100? people

8. How much is 175.639 ml of milk to the nearest whole number? ml

9. An apple weighs 100.364 grams.
Round this weight to the nearest tenth of a gram. grams

10. Matt is 159.67 cm tall. What is this to the nearest whole centimetre? Circle the correct answer.

    A   152 cm   B   157 cm   C   160 cm   D   150 cm   E   159 cm

11. Which of the options below will equal 1000? Circle the correct answer.
    A   1652 rounded to the nearest 1000
    B   847 rounded to the nearest 100
    C   956 rounded to the nearest 100
    D   987 rounded to the nearest 10

/ 11

Lily is using a digger to create a flower bed and a sand pit in her garden.

12. Using her digger, Lily moves 1.243 tonnes of soil to make
a new flower bed. How much soil is this to one decimal place? tonnes

13. Next, Lily moves 0.337 tonnes of sand to make a sandpit.
How much is this to two decimal places? tonnes

14. Lily moves 0.5 tonnes of pebbles to decorate the flower bed. If this mass has been
rounded to one decimal place, which of these could be the actual mass of pebbles?

    A   0.351 tonnes   B   0.562 tonnes   C   0.545 tonnes   D   0.445 tonnes

15. Using your answer from question 14, round the
actual mass of pebbles to two decimal places. tonnes

/ 4

Section One — Working with Numbers

4

Addition

Look at the menu on the right and work out how much it would cost to buy the following items:

Menu	
Sandwich	£2.00
Teacake	£1.35
Scone	£1.85
Tea	£1.40
Coffee	£1.25
Orange juice	£1.50

1.   A sandwich and an orange juice.   £ ⬜.⬜⬜

2.   Tea and a teacake.   £ ⬜.⬜⬜

3.   Coffee and a scone.   £ ⬜.⬜⬜

4.   Orange juice and a scone.   £ ⬜.⬜⬜

5.   A scone and a teacake.   £ ⬜.⬜⬜

Hint: If you add the decimals using the column method, remember to line up the decimal points.

Work out the answer to each calculation.

6.   428 + 23   ⬜⬜⬜

7.   6.4 + 3.7   ⬜⬜.⬜⬜

8.   8.5 + 16.3   ⬜⬜.⬜⬜

9.   12.5 + 26.7   ⬜⬜.⬜⬜

10.   12.5 + 3.72   ⬜⬜.⬜⬜

11.   13.9 + 3.43   ⬜⬜.⬜⬜

12.   Jamie is 147 cm tall, Micky is 149 cm and Kyle is 151 cm. What is the total height of the three boys in centimetres?   ⬜⬜⬜ cm

13.   Latisha has a 50p coin, six 20p coins, a 5p coin and four 2p coins. How much money does she have in pounds?   £ ⬜.⬜⬜   / 13

A farmer is loading some sheep onto two trailers. The sheep have been divided as follows:

Trailer A	Trailer B
Shaun — 80.2 kg,	Sara — 64.9 kg,
Sally — 52 kg,	Sadie — 58.1 kg,
Stan — 73.4 kg	Sammy — 72.8 kg

14.   What is the total weight of the sheep on trailer A?   ⬜⬜⬜.⬜ kg

15.   What is the total weight of the sheep on trailer B?   ⬜⬜⬜.⬜ kg

16.   The weight allowance for each trailer is 250 kg. The farmer needs to load one more sheep, which weighs 44.3 kg. Which trailer could he put it on to?   / 3

   A Trailer A   **B** Trailer B   **C** Either trailer   **D** Neither trailer

Section One — Working with Numbers

Subtraction

Work out the answer to each calculation.

1. 76 − 25 ☐☐

2. 67 − 18 ☐☐

3. 112 − 83 ☐☐

4. 120 − 103 ☐☐

5. 18.3 − 12.6 ☐☐.☐

Hint: One way of tackling subtraction calculations is to use partitioning. But sometimes it's quicker to use a different method, such as counting up.

Work out how much change you would receive from a £5 note if you spent the following amounts:

6. £3.55 £ ☐☐.☐☐

7. 89p £ ☐☐.☐☐

8. £4.37 £ ☐☐.☐☐

9. £2.08 £ ☐☐.☐☐

10. £1.11 £ ☐☐.☐☐

/ 10

11. Sam is going on holiday. His suitcase can carry 25 kg. If he has already packed 15.7 kg, what is the maximum weight he can add to his suitcase? Circle the correct answer.

    A 9.7 kg   **B** 9.3 kg   **C** 12.8 kg   **D** 10.3 kg   **E** 8.7 kg

12. Frankie had £20.35. He bought a football magazine for £1.80 and an ice cream for £1.25. How much money did he have left?

    £ ☐☐.☐☐

Look at the sweet shop price list on the right.

13. If Helen has £2.60, how much change will she have if she buys a packet of flying saucers and a packet of cola bottles?

    £ ☐☐.☐☐

14. Megan has £5.30. She buys 3 packets of white mice. How much change does she get?

    £ ☐☐.☐☐

PRICE LIST	
Sherbet	50p
Fizzy laces	70p
Cola bottles	89p
White mice	£1.20
Fried eggs	70p
Flying saucers	£1.10

15. Megan then buys two more items. Which of these could she have bought?

    A Flying saucers and fried eggs   **C** White mice and sherbet
    B Fizzy laces and flying saucers   **D** Cola bottles and white mice

/ 5

Section One — Working with Numbers

Multiplying and Dividing by 10, 100 and 1000

Work out the answer to each calculation.

1. $27 \times 100 =$ ☐☐☐☐☐

2. $350 \times 10 =$ ☐☐☐☐

3. $7.84 \times 100 =$ ☐☐☐☐

4. $65.5 \times 10 =$ ☐☐☐☐☐

5. $0.4 \times 1000 =$ ☐☐☐☐☐

6. $83.5 \times 100 =$ ☐☐☐☐☐

7. $2314 \div$ ☐☐☐☐ $=$ 23.14

8. $72.40 \div$ ☐☐☐☐ $=$ 0.0724

9. $820 \div$ ☐☐☐☐ $=$ 82

10. $192.4 \div$ ☐☐☐☐ $=$ 1.924

/ 10

11. Cecil charges 85p for one iced cupcake.
    If he sells 100 cupcakes, how much money
    will he receive in pounds?

    £ ☐☐.☐☐

12. There are 1548 children at Dinah's school.
    Homework planners come in boxes of 10.
    How many boxes should the school order so that there are
    enough homework planners for every child to have one?

    ☐☐☐☐☐ boxes

13. Patrick thinks of a number. He first multiplies it
    by 10 and then divides his answer by 1000. He ends
    up with 1.3. What number did he start off with?

    ☐☐☐☐☐

14. $1250 = 1000 \times$ ____
    What number is missing from the equation above?
    Circle the correct answer.

    A 125   **B** 125 000   **C** 12 500   **D** 1.25   **E** 12.5

15. 1283 _____ $= 0.1283 \times 100$
    Which of the following should go in the gap in the equation above?
    Circle the correct answer.

    A × 10   **B** × 100   **C** × 1000   **D** ÷ 100   **E** ÷ 1000

    / 5

Section One — Working with Numbers

Multiplication

Work out the answer to each calculation.

1. $36 \times 5 =$ ☐☐☐

2. $19 \times 4 =$ ☐☐☐

3. $3 \times 1.5 =$ ☐☐.☐☐

4. $6 \times 3.5 =$ ☐☐.☐☐

5. $2.25 \times 4 =$ ☐☐.☐☐

6. $7.4 \times 3 =$ ☐☐.☐☐

A number machine multiplies numbers by 12.
What number comes out when the following numbers are put in?

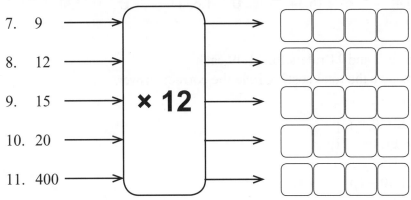

7. 9

8. 12

9. 15

10. 20

11. 400

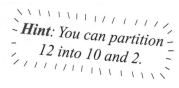

Hint: You can partition 12 into 10 and 2.

/ 11

12. Which of the following is equal to 12.6×5.5? Circle the correct answer.

   A 0.0693   **C** 6.93   **E** 693
   B 0.693   **D** 69.3

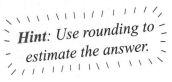

Hint: Use rounding to estimate the answer.

13. $420 + 420 + 420 + 420 + 420 + 420 = 210 \times \underline{\quad}$

   Circle the missing number.

   A 8   **B** 12   **C** 16   **D** 20   **E** 24

14. Bella buys 5 chewy bars at 29p each. What is the total cost in pounds?  £ ☐☐.☐☐

15. Zac buys 3 packets of crisps at 45p each and 4 toffee crunches at 25p each. What is the total cost in pounds?  £ ☐☐.☐☐

16. 1 measure of car shampoo must be diluted with 6 measures of water. How much water should be added to 120 ml of car shampoo? ☐☐☐ ml

17. $\boxed{250 \times 8 = 2000}$ What is 250×0.008?   ☐.☐☐☐  / 6

Section One — Working with Numbers

Multiplication

18. Sarah buys a comic costing £1.50 each month.
     How much does Sarah spend on comics in three years?

£

19. Three friends hire a bike each for four hours. If the bikes
     cost £5.50 each per hour, what will their total bill be?

£

20. $\boxed{4.3 \times 3.8 = 16.34}$

     What is 43×0.38? Circle the correct answer.

     A 1634   **B** 163.4   **C** 16.34   **D** 1.634   **E** 0.1634

21. Iqbal buys 26 pens for 98p each and 11 rulers for £1.49 each.
     Which of these calculations give the total cost? Circle the correct answer.

     A $26 \times £1 - 26p + 11 \times £1.50 - 11p$
     B $26 \times £1 + 52p + 11 \times £1.50 + 11p$
     C $26 \times 98p - 52p + 11 \times £1.49 - 11p$
     D $26 \times £1 - 52p + 11 \times £1.50 - 11p$
     E $11 \times £1 - 2p + 26 \times £1.50 - 1p$

22. $\boxed{75 \times 231 = 17\ 325}$

     What is 75×462? Circle the correct answer.

     A 346 500   **B** 3465   **C** 35 000   **D** 34 650   **E** 34 000

23. What is 0.7×0.8?

     Hint: Use the answer to 7×8 to help you work out 0.7×0.8.

24. $\boxed{2025 = 45 \times 45}$

     Which of the following calculations is equal to 4050? Circle the correct answer.

     A 90×90
     B $45 \times 45 \times 45$
     C 90×45
     D 90×22.5
     E 22.5×45

25. Packs of toilet rolls cost 80p. There are 4 rolls in a pack.
     Mr Lewis wants to stock up but only has £10.
     How many toilet rolls can he buy?

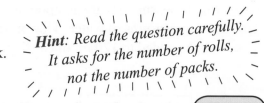

Hint: Read the question carefully. It asks for the number of rolls, not the number of packs.

rolls   / 8

Division

Work out the answer to each calculation.

1. 48 ÷ 8

3. 72 ÷ 9

5. 51 ÷ 3

2. 56 ÷ 7

4. 66 ÷ 6

6. 36 ÷ 9

Adam, Amy and Alfie are triplets. On their birthday, they were given some amounts of money to share equally. Work out how much money each triplet receives from each person.

7. Their grandma gave them £60.   £ ⬜⬜.⬜⬜

8. Their uncle gave them £45.   £ ⬜⬜.⬜⬜

9. Their mother gave them £99.   £ ⬜⬜.⬜⬜

10. Their brother gave them £9.99.   £ ⬜⬜.⬜⬜

11. Their aunt gave them £10.50.   £ ⬜⬜.⬜⬜

/ 11

Jane's wedding cake has a mass of 3000 g.

12. The cake is cut into slices with a mass of 40 g each. How many slices are there?

13. Jane has enough cake for each guest to have three slices of cake. How many guests does Jane have?

14. If Jane decides to reduce the mass of her cake to 2000 g, how many 40 g slices can each guest have?

Adil paid £72 for four terms of swimming lessons.

15. What is the cost for each term of lessons?   £ ⬜⬜.⬜⬜

16. There are 12 lessons in each term. What is the cost of each lesson?   £ ⬜⬜.⬜⬜

17. Jason shares a bag of biscuits equally between seven dogs. There are some biscuits left over. Which of these numbers cannot be the number of biscuits left over? Circle the correct answer.

   A 7   **B** 6   **C** 5   **D** 4   **E** 3

18. Sita divides a number by a smaller number. Her answer has a remainder of 5. Which of these numbers could Sita have divided by?

   A 5   **B** 6   **C** 4   **D** 2   **E** 3

/ 7

Section One — Working with Numbers

Mixed Calculations

Write down the answer to each calculation.

1. $(37 + 13) \times 3 =$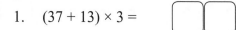

2. $56 + (29 - 17) =$

3. $150 \div (18 + 12) =$

4. $235 - (3 \times 7) =$

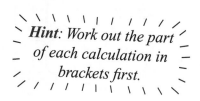

Hint: Work out the part of each calculation in brackets first.

5. What is $79 \times 365 + 365 \times 21$? Circle the correct answer.

   A 8 300   B 17 300   C 19 989   D 36 500   E 73 000

   / 5

The table shows the prices charged at a play centre. Answer the following questions.

Entry Prices	Baby (Age 6 to 12 months)	£1.50
	Toddler (Age 1 to 3 years)	£2.25
	Child (Age 4 to 14 years)	£3.25
Extras	Go-Kart Ride	£1.50
	Snack Pack	£1.00

6. How much would entry for one toddler and two children cost?

   £ ⬜ ⬜ . ⬜ ⬜

7. Three 14 year olds each pay for entry to the play centre and a go-kart ride. Which of these calculations could be used to work out the total amount they paid? Circle the correct answer.

   A $3 \times 2.25 + 3 \times 1.00$ C $3.25 + 3 \times 1.50$ E $3 \times 3.25 + 3 \times 1.50$
   B $3 \times 3.25 + 1.50$ D $3 \times 1.50 + 3 \times 1.00$

8. David buys entry for two children and pays for two go-kart rides and two snack packs. How much change will he receive from a £20 note?

   £

9. Which of these calculations does not equal 81? Circle the correct answer.

   A $39 + 25 \times 2 - 8$ C $21 + 100 \div 2 + 10$ E $10 \times 5 + 8 + 23$
   B $50 + 31 \times 1$ D $50 \times 10 + 39 - 8$

Peter collects 1400 g of blackberries. He gives 200 g to Lena, and divides the rest equally to make 4 pies.

10. How many grams of blackberries are in each pie?

     grams

11. Instead of making his 4 pies, Peter eats 45 g of the remaining blackberries and divides the rest equally to make 3 pies. How many grams of blackberries are in each pie?

    grams

12. Becky can make 400 ml of lemonade out of one lemon. If she uses 6 lemons to make lemonade, but drinks one 600 ml glass of it, how much lemonade does she have left?

     ml   / 7

Section One — Working with Numbers

Types of Number

Circle the smallest number in each row below.

1. 5   −2   0.5   −5   2.5

2. −9   −7   7   −1   9

3. −1   −18   −10   0   −28

4. −20   −30   −24   −26   −22

5. −1   1.5   0.1   0.05   0.15

Choose one number from this list of numbers to fill in the gaps below.

   −13   6.5   20   6.65   −7   64.5   22   −11   21   98

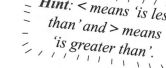

Hint: < means 'is less than' and > means 'is greater than'.

6. ⬚⬚ > 68

7. ⬚⬚⬚ < −12

8. 65 > ⬚⬚⬚⬚ > 64

9. 20 < ⬚⬚ < 22

10. −12 < ⬚⬚⬚ < −8

11. 6.9 > ⬚⬚⬚⬚ > 6.5

/ 11

12. Circle the statement which is incorrect.

   A $−5 < 8 − 10$ **C** $6 > −3 + 9$ **E** $−1 = 3 − 4$
   B $−3 > −7 + 3$ **D** $−4 > 3 − 8$

13. Kat throws three darts. The total score of the three darts has to be an even number for her to win the game. Which set of dart scores would not give her a winning total? Circle the correct answer.

   A   34, 28, 12   **C**   60, 54, 8   **E**   22, 48, 36
   B   33, 27, 50   **D**   13, 21, 57

14. Amy is 3^2 years old and her grandma is 8^2 years old.
   What is the difference between their ages?   ⬚⬚ years

15. Rob plays a game where he rolls five dice. The total score of the five dice has to be a square number for him to win the game. On which set of rolls would he win the game? Circle the correct answer.

   A   2, 4, 5, 3, 5   **C**   1, 4, 2, 6, 3   **E**   3, 2, 1, 4, 5
   B   6, 3, 3, 5, 1   **D**   6, 5, 1, 4, 5

16. Darren thinks of a number and squares it. The answer is 11 less than the next square number.
   Circle the number Darren was thinking of.

   A   3   **B**   4   **C**   5   **D**   6   **E**   7

/ 5

Factors, Multiples and Primes

Write down the first four multiples of each number given below.

1. 4   ☐ , ☐ , ☐☐ , ☐☐

2. 6   ☐ , ☐☐ , ☐☐ , ☐☐

3. 7   ☐ , ☐☐ , ☐☐ , ☐☐

4. 9   ☐ , ☐☐ , ☐☐ , ☐☐

In each row below, circle the number which is a multiple of 3 and 4.

5. 9   15   16   28   36

6. 11   17   21   24   29

7. 12   13   22   27   31

/ 7

8. Which number is in the wrong place in this Venn diagram? Circle the correct answer.

    A   7   C   64   E   28
    B   12   D   21

9. Which of these numbers is a common factor of 18 and 24? Circle the correct answer.

    A 4   B 5   C 6   D 8   E 9

10. What is the sum of all the prime numbers between 1 and 10?   ☐☐

11. Sara adds five to the largest prime number below 20. What answer should she get?   ☐☐

12. Which of the following lists of numbers would go into the empty box in this sorting diagram? Circle the correct answer.

	Prime	Not Prime
Even	2	4, 10, 12, 28
Odd	7, 11, 13, 19	

    A   3, 5, 9, 11   C   5, 8, 12, 14
    B   3, 11, 27, 31   D   9, 13, 18, 21   E   9, 15, 21, 33

13. Lucy drew this sorting diagram. Her teacher pointed out that one number can go in two places in the diagram. Which number is it? Circle the correct answer.

	Factor of 18	Prime
< 10		
> 10		

    A 1   B 6   C 5   D 3   E 9

14. Which of these multiples of 3 add up to make a factor of 36? Circle the correct answer.

    A   3 and 12   C   3 and 15   E   9 and 12
    B   6 and 21   D   6 and 27

/ 7

Section Two — Number Knowledge

Fractions

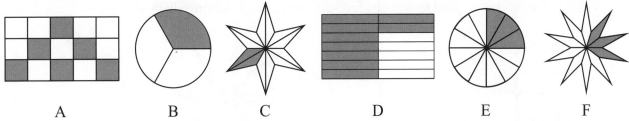

A   B   C   D   E   F

A fraction of each of these shapes is shaded. Write down the letter of the shape which has each of the following fractions shaded.

1. $\frac{1}{3}$ ☐

2. $\frac{1}{4}$ ☐

3. $\frac{9}{14}$ ☐

4. $\frac{3}{10}$ ☐

5. $\frac{6}{15}$ ☐

6. $\frac{1}{6}$ ☐

A tin contains 24 biscuits and is shared between 5 people.
Write down how many biscuits each person gets.

7. Dan's share is $\frac{1}{6}$ of the biscuits. ☐

8. Ally's share is $\frac{1}{4}$ of the biscuits. ☐

9. Molly's share is $\frac{1}{12}$ of the biscuits. ☐

10. George's share is $\frac{1}{8}$ of the biscuits. ☐

11. Maya's share is $\frac{3}{8}$ of the biscuits. ☐

/ 11

12. Joe, Marcus, Alan and John put together their spending money to buy 12 doughnuts. They receive another box of 12 doughnuts for free. If each boy takes 5 doughnuts, what fraction of the total number of doughnuts are left? Circle the correct answer

    A $\frac{4}{12}$ B $\frac{20}{24}$ C $\frac{6}{24}$ D $\frac{1}{6}$ E $\frac{6}{12}$

13. Circle the largest fraction.

    A $\frac{1}{2}$ B $\frac{5}{12}$ C $\frac{2}{3}$ D $\frac{5}{6}$ E $\frac{1}{3}$

14. How many fifths are there in 11? Circle the correct answer.

    A 11   B 15   C 22   D 34   E 55

15. Lisa is painting her fence. Her fence has 18 posts. Lisa paints $\frac{1}{3}$ of them red. How many posts were not painted red? ☐☐

16. The local library's membership is made up of 50 women and 40 men. What fraction of the total membership is made up of men? Circle the correct answer.

    A $\frac{1}{40}$ B $\frac{4}{5}$ C $\frac{50}{90}$ D $\frac{5}{4}$ E $\frac{4}{9}$

/ 5

Ratio and Proportion

What is the ratio of shaded to non-shaded sections in the following shapes?

1. 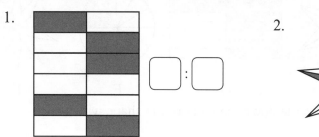 ☐ : ☐

2. 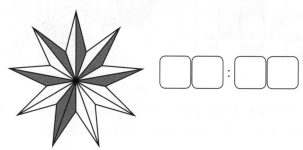 ☐☐ : ☐☐

3. Clive can paint 3 pictures every 2 hours.
   How long will it take him to paint 24 pictures? ☐☐ hours

4. While walking to school, Andreas found that 1 in every 9 cars that drove by him were red.
   8 red cars drove by him.
   What was the total number of cars that drove by Andreas? ☐☐ cars

Divide 48 into the following ratios.

5. 1:3 ☐☐ : ☐☐

6. 5:1 ☐☐ : ☐☐

7. 3:5 ☐☐ : ☐☐

8. 1:11 ☐☐ : ☐☐

9. 2:1 ☐☐ : ☐☐

10. 13:3 ☐☐ : ☐☐

/ 10

Chloe is baking some cupcakes. A recipe to make 8 cupcakes requires 4 eggs, 250 grams of flour, 300 grams of butter and 350 grams of sugar.

11. How many cupcakes would 900 grams of butter make?

12. How many eggs would Chloe need to make 32 cupcakes?

13. Chloe wants to make 20 cakes.
    How many grams of flour will she need? Circle the correct answer.
    A 500 **B** 625 **C** 675 **D** 550 **E** 750

14. A zookeeper is counting the animals in the reptile house.
    He counts 11 snakes and finds that there are 5 more lizards than snakes.
    What is the ratio of snakes to lizards? ☐☐ : ☐☐

 / 4

Section Two — Number Knowledge

Percentages, Fractions and Decimals

Write the following decimals as percentages.

1. 0.5 ☐☐ %   3. 0.21 ☐☐ %

2. 0.1 ☐☐ %   4. 0.03 ☐☐ %

Write the following fractions as decimals.

5. ¾ ☐.☐☐   7. ³⁄₁₀ ☐.☐☐

6. ⅖ ☐.☐☐   8. ¹¹⁄₂₀ ☐.☐☐

Write the following percentages as fractions in their simplest form.

9. 15 % ☐☐/☐☐   10. 85 % ☐☐/☐☐

/ 10

A fraction of each of the following shapes has been shaded.

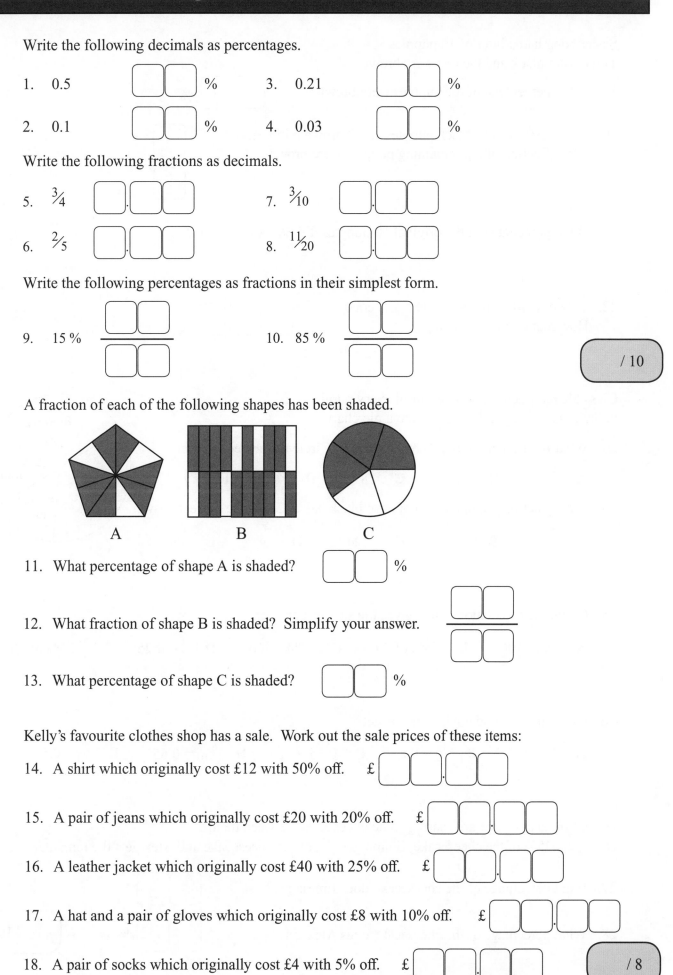

A   B   C

11. What percentage of shape A is shaded? ☐☐ %

12. What fraction of shape B is shaded? Simplify your answer. ☐☐/☐☐

13. What percentage of shape C is shaded? ☐☐ %

Kelly's favourite clothes shop has a sale. Work out the sale prices of these items:

14. A shirt which originally cost £12 with 50% off. £ ☐☐.☐☐

15. A pair of jeans which originally cost £20 with 20% off. £ ☐☐.☐☐

16. A leather jacket which originally cost £40 with 25% off. £ ☐☐.☐☐

17. A hat and a pair of gloves which originally cost £8 with 10% off. £ ☐☐.☐☐

18. A pair of socks which originally cost £4 with 5% off. £ ☐☐.☐☐

/ 8

Section Two — Number Knowledge

Percentages, Fractions and Decimals

Sasha's dog had a litter of 10 puppies.
Three were black and the rest were brown.

19. What percentage of the puppies were brown? ☐☐ %

20. Sasha gave away 2 black puppies and 2 brown puppies.
    What fraction of the remaining puppies were brown? ☐/☐

21. What percentage of the original 10 puppies did Sasha give away? ☐☐ %

22. 15% of a 50 gram chocolate bar is cocoa.
    How many grams is this? ☐☐.☐ g

Class 5K recorded the hair colour of every pupil
in their class and put the results into a pie chart.

23. What fraction of the pupils had red hair? Circle the correct answer.

    A $\frac{1}{5}$ **B** $\frac{1}{10}$ **C** $\frac{1}{8}$ **D** $\frac{1}{6}$ **E** $\frac{2}{9}$

24. What fraction of pupils did not have black hair? Circle the correct answer.

    A $\frac{7}{8}$ **B** $\frac{7}{10}$ **C** $\frac{13}{20}$ **D** $\frac{7}{9}$ **E** $\frac{5}{6}$

Pie chart: Brown 40%, Black 35%, Blonde 15%, Red

25. Circle the calculation which gives the smallest answer.

    A $\frac{1}{4}$ of 100   **B** 75% of 80   **C** 50% of 60   **D** $\frac{3}{5}$ of 25   **E** 25% of 40

26. Circle the statement which is correct.

    A $\frac{1}{5} > 0.2$ **B** $\frac{1}{2} = 0.2$ **C** $0.35 > \frac{1}{4}$ **D** $\frac{6}{10} = 0.65$ **E** $\frac{2}{5} > 0.5$

Dave, Emma and Alex are sharing some cheesecake between them.
Dave gets 35% of the cheesecake, Emma gets $\frac{2}{5}$ of the cheesecake and Alex gets the remainder.

27. What percentage of the cheesecake does Emma get? ☐☐ %

28. What percentage of the cheesecake does Alex get? ☐☐ %   / 10

Section Two — Number Knowledge

Algebra

If □ = 4, work out the value of the following expressions.

Hint: If a number and a symbol are next to each other, you need to multiply them together.

1. 56 − □ ☐☐

2. 73 + □ ☐☐

3. 6□ ☐☐

4. 32 ÷ □ ☐☐

5. 3□ − 2 ☐☐

6. 4□ + 5 ☐☐

/ 6

7. Gaby is ◇ years old. Her mum is 24 years older. Which expression gives Gaby's mum's age in years? Circle the correct answer.

    A ◇ − 24   **B** ◇ + 24   **C** 24◇   **D** 24 − ◇   **E** 24 ÷ ◇

8. A football club are ordering kits for the new season. The cost, in pounds, of *y* kits is given by the expression 15 + 8*y*. How much will it cost the club if they order 20 kits?

    £

9. Mr Ali is ordering some maths books over the internet. The books cost £3 each and the postage is £4.99 for an order of any size. Which expression gives the cost, in pounds, of ordering ⊙ books? Circle the correct answer.

    A 3⊙ + 4.99⊙   **B** 3⊙   **C** 3 + 4.99⊙   **D** 3⊙ − 4.99   **E** 3⊙ + 4.99

10. Heather is comparing the cost, in pounds, of hiring cleaners. Cleaner A charges 7*h* + 20. Cleaner B charges 4*h* + 25. If she hires a cleaner for 5 hours (*h*), what would the difference in cost be between the two cleaners?

    £

Find the value of ⬟ in each of the following:

11. ⬟ + 7 = 20   ⬟ = ☐☐

12. 7 − ⬟ = −2   ⬟ = ☐☐

13. 9⬟ = 45   ⬟ = ☐☐

14. 36 ÷ ⬟ = 6   ⬟ = ☐☐

15. Kit wants to bake 10 cookies, but he only has 250 g of flour. The amount of flour, in grams, needed to bake different types of cookies can be worked out using the formulas below (☆ stands for the number of cookies). Which type of cookies can he make? Circle the correct answer.

    A Chocolate cookies: 19☆ + 75
    B Raspberry cookies: 22☆ + 35
    C Coconut cookies: 23☆ + 25
    D Hazelnut cookies: 30☆ + 5
    E Caramel cookies: 20☆ + 45

/ 9

Number Sequences

Write down the next number in each sequence.

1. 8   16   24   32   ☐☐

2. 27   24   21   18   ☐☐

3. 11   33   55   77   ☐☐

4. 48   60   72   84   ☐☐

Write down the fourth number in the sequence which follows each rule below.
The first one has already been done for you.

Example: Start at –17, count on in steps of 2.   –| 1 | 1 |

5. Start at 1, double the previous number.   ☐☐

6. Start at 20, count back in steps of 8.   –☐☐

7. Start at 2.5, count on in steps of 2.5.   ☐☐

The expression $3n - 1$ can be used to find the nth term in a number sequence.
Use the expression to find each of the following terms in the sequence.

8. The 1st term.   ☐☐

9. The 6th term.   ☐☐

10. The 15th term.   ☐☐

11. The 20th term.   ☐☐

/ 11

12. Chris is building a tower out of rectangular blocks. The tower has
3 rows and there are 9 blocks on the bottom row. How many blocks
would there be on the bottom row of a tower with 6 rows?

☐☐☐ blocks

13. Polly starts with a number between 5 and 10. She counts up in steps of 5
until she reaches 38. What number did she start off with?   ☐☐

14. Ashley started at the number 3 and made a sequence by doubling the number each time.
Which of these numbers were in her sequence? Circle the correct answer.

A 9, 30   B 15, 48   C 12, 36   D 20, 38   E 12, 48

15. Amira writes the following sequence on the whiteboard, but rubs out the first and last numbers:

___   1.75   2.5   3.25   4   ___

What are the missing numbers? Circle the correct answer.

A 0.5 and 4.75   B 0 and 5   C 1 and 4.75   D 1.5 and 5.5   E 0.75 and 5.25

/ 4

Section Three — Number Problems

Word Problems

1. One banana and three mangos cost £2.30.
   The banana costs 80p. How much does one mango cost?

   £ ☐☐.☐☐

2. Dina bought five different pairs of shoes that cost £25.00 each.
   She decided to keep two pairs and returned the others.
   How much money was she refunded for the shoes she returned?

   £ ☐☐.☐☐

3. Jo's gerbil has 20 g of food each day. Each packet of food contains 250 g.
   Jo buys four packets. How many days will this food last?

   ☐☐☐ days

4. Mrs Cooper fills her car up with diesel. She pays with two £20 pound notes
   and receives £11.63 change. How much did the fuel for the car cost?

   £ ☐☐.☐☐

The board on the right shows the price of items in a stationery shop.

5. Henry has £1.60 to buy stationery for school. Which of these does he
   have exactly the right amount of money to buy? Circle the correct answer.

Pens	70p each
Pencils	55p each
Rubbers	35p each

   A 2 pencils and 1 rubber **D** 1 pencil, 1 rubber and 1 pen
   B 3 pencils **E** 1 pencil, 2 rubbers and 1 pen
   C 1 pen and 2 rubbers

6. How much change would Becky have left
   from £6.65 if she bought 2 of each item?

   £ ☐☐.☐☐

7. A box of crisps contains 6 packets of ready salted crisps, 3 packets of cheese and onion crisps,
   2 packets of salt and vinegar crisps and 1 packet of prawn cocktail crisps.
   If you choose a bag at random, which of these statements is correct?
   Circle the correct answer.

   Hint: Start by working out how many packets of crisps are in the box.

   A You have an even chance of picking cheese and onion crisps.
   B You have a less than even chance of picking ready salted crisps.
   C You have a more than even chance of picking salt and vinegar crisps.
   D You are less likely to pick cheese and onion crisps than ready salted crisps.
   E You are less likely to pick salt and vinegar crisps than prawn cocktail crisps.

8. A shop pays £15.00 for 20 kg of potatoes. They charge customers £1.20 per kilogram of potatoes.
   If the shop sells all of the potatoes, what will be the difference between the amount of money they
   spent and the amount of money they earned selling potatoes? Circle the correct answer.

   A £15 **B** £9 **C** £16 **D** £12 **E** £20

9. Zac and Isa are making party bags for 13 children. They put
   three different toys into each bag. The toys come in packs of
   nine. How many packs will Zac and Isa need to buy?

   ☐☐ packs

10. A clothes shop has a sale. The price of every item is reduced by half every week.
    A jacket that had originally cost £148 has now been reduced to £18.50.
    How many weeks has the jacket been in the sale? Circle the correct answer.

    A 3 **B** 2 **C** 7 **D** 5 **E** 4

    / 10

Word Problems

11. Alexa is making bracelets. She needs 10 beads and a wire strip for each bracelet. The beads cost 45p each, and the wire costs 75p a strip. How much will it cost her to make three bracelets?

£ ☐☐.☐☐

12. Cameron makes a tower using the 10p coins in his money box. Each 10p coin is 2 mm thick and the tower is 13 cm high. What is the total value of the 10p coins in the tower?

£ ☐☐.☐☐

The prices at Eastcliff ice cream shop are summarised in the table below.

1 scoop of ice cream	£1.75
2 scoops of ice cream	£3.25
Ice cream sandwich	£3.45
Slush drink	£1.99

13. Oliver buys one of each thing on the menu. How much change will Oliver receive from £15?

£ ☐☐.☐☐

14. Rae has £5. She wants to buy 2 slush drinks and 1 scoop of ice cream. How much more money will she need?

£ ☐☐.☐☐

15. Grace has enough space on her MP3 player to store 45 minutes of music. Each song is between 2 minutes and 3 minutes long. What is the minimum number of songs she will be able to store? Circle the correct answer.

A   22   B   12   C   25   D   15   E   9

16. Ant thinks of a number. He doubles the number and then multiplies the answer by itself. He then adds 15 and is left with 51. What number did he start with?

☐☐

17. A supermarket sells a pack of four peppers for £1.80 or a pack of six peppers for £2.52. What is the cheapest amount you could pay per pepper?

£ ☐☐.☐☐

18. Mr Habib plants 55 bulbs in his garden ready for spring. They are a mixture of daffodils and tulips. Circle the statement that cannot be true.

A   There are 5 fewer tulips than daffodils.
B   There are 13 more daffodils than tulips.
C   There are more daffodils than tulips.
D   There are 8 more tulips than daffodils.
E   There are more tulips than daffodils.

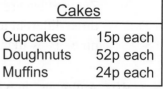

The table below shows the prices of some cakes at the Overdon bakery.

Cakes	
Cupcakes	15p each
Doughnuts	52p each
Muffins	24p each

19. Laura is buying cakes for 20 people. She decides to buy enough cakes so that each person can have one cupcake and half of a doughnut. How much will she spend altogether on the cakes?

£ ☐☐.☐☐

20. Luke has £10. He buys 15 doughnuts. With the remaining money, how many muffins can he buy?

☐☐ muffins

/ 10

Section Three — Number Problems

Data Tables

This table shows the scores of five children in a spelling test. The test was out of 50.

George	Paula	Sanjay	Kate	Nina
37	19	25	39	43

1. Who scored the highest mark? Circle the correct answer.

     A George   **B** Paula   **C** Sanjay   **D** Kate   **E** Nina

2. Who scored exactly 20 less than Kate? Circle the correct answer.

     A George   **B** Paula   **C** Sanjay   **D** Nina

3. Find the difference for the scores in the spelling test for Nina and Paula.

4. How many marks did George lose?

The table below shows part of a train timetable for a train running between Appleford and Banbridge.

	Train A	Train B	Train C	Train D
Depart Appleford	09:00	10:30	12:00	14:30
Arrive in Banbridge	11:15	12:00	14:45	16:15

5. Robert has to be in Banbridge by 12:15.
    What is the latest train that he could catch from Appleford? Circle the correct answer.

     Train A   Train B   Train C   Train D

6. Which train takes the longest time? Circle the correct answer.

     Train A   Train B   Train C   Train D

7. Which train takes the shortest time? Circle the correct answer.

     Train A   Train B   Train C   Train D

The table shows the number of animals in one tank at an aquarium.

Otters	4
Rays	16
Eels	25
Turtles	12
Squid	3
Crabs	43
Lobsters	9
Starfish	76

8. Which of these statements is true? Circle the correct answer.

   A   There are twice as many lobsters as otters.

   B   There are more rays and eels than crabs.

   C   There are 25 fewer turtles than crabs.

   D   There are 4 times as many turtles as squid.

   E   There are 143 animals in total.

9. How many more eels are there than otters?

10. What is the total number of crabs, lobsters and starfish in the tank?

/ 10

Data Tables

The table shows the finishing times of six children in the 50 m sprint race at sports day.

Child	Alan	Marg	Carol	Ranjit	Ahmed	Louisa
Time (secs)	12.8	14.5	15.3	16.2	10.9	11.1

11. Which child came in third place? Circle the correct answer.

     A Alan   **B** Marg   **C** Carol   **D** Ranjit   **E** Ahmed   **F** Louisa

12. Who finished 2.5 seconds after Alan? Circle the correct answer.

     A Marg   **B** Carol   **C** Ranjit   **D** Ahmed   **E** Louisa

13. How much slower was Marg than Louisa? ⬚.⬚ seconds

The table shows the number of points scored by archers in a competition.

14. Which of these statements is true? Circle the correct answer.

Points scored	Frequency
0 - 5	9
6 - 10	12
11 - 15	19
16 - 20	13
21 - 25	5

     A   18 archers scored more than 15 points.

     B   Half of the archers scored between 11 and 15 points.

     C   20 archers scored between 0 and 10 points.

     D   Less than half the archers scored between 6 and 20 points.

     E   60 archers took part in the competition.

15. What was the most frequent score? Circle the correct answer.

     A 0 - 5   **B** 6 - 10   **C** 11 - 15   **D** 16 - 20   **E** 21 - 25

16. Archers who score 11 or more go through to the next round.
How many more archers got through than didn't get through? ⬚⬚

Kylie is ordering some cakes. She has only filled in some parts of the order form.

Cake	Quantity	Price	Total
Lemon Drizzle	2	£2.00	£4.00
Victoria Sponge	1	£1.50	
Fruit Cake		£3.00	
		Total	£11.50

17. How many fruit cakes has Kylie ordered? ⬚⬚

18. What would the total cost be if she added 2 more
fruit cakes and one more Victoria sponge to her order? £⬚⬚.⬚⬚   /8

Displaying Data

The bar chart shows the number of children in five classes.

1. Which class has the fewest children in?   P ☐

2. How many children are there in class P2?   ☐ ☐

3. Which two classes have more than 28 children?   P ☐ and P ☐

4. How many more children are there in P3 than P4?   ☐ ☐

Hint: Read across from the top of a bar to the vertical axis to find out how many children it shows.

5. Frankie asked 19 people whether they prefer tea, coffee or hot chocolate. His results are shown in this pictogram.

   How many people said they prefer tea?   ☐ ☐

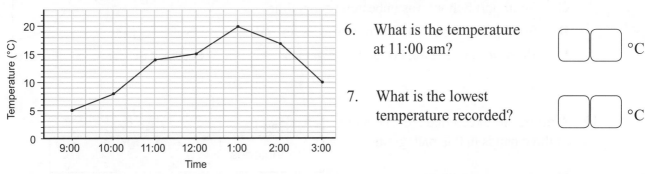

6. What is the temperature at 11:00 am?   ☐ ☐ °C

7. What is the lowest temperature recorded?   ☐ ☐ °C

This line graph shows the temperature inside a gardener's greenhouse during part of a day.

8. Between which two times does the temperature rise the most?   Circle the correct answer.

   A   9:00 and 10:00   **C**   11:00 and 12:00   **E**   1:00 and 2:00
   B   10:00 and 11:00   **D**   12:00 and 1:00

9. A group of tourists were asked in a survey to name their favourite English city. This bar chart shows the results.

   How many people took part in the survey?
   Circle the correct number.

   A   84   **C**   102   **E**   120
   B   92   **D**   110

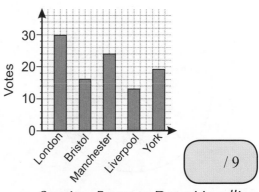

/ 9

Section Four — Data Handling

Displaying Data

10. This line graph shows how the height of a building changes as the number of floors it has increases.

    Using the graph, work out how tall a block of flats with 14 floors would be.

     m

    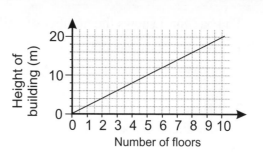

11. This dual bar chart shows the number of hours Sam and Sanjay worked out at the Fitness Centre over a three-week period.

    Over the three weeks, how many more hours did Sam spend working out than Sanjay?

     hours

    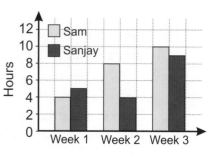

12. The pie charts below show the results of two schools in a rugby tournament. Each school played 32 matches. Which of these statements is true?

    Circle the correct answer.

    A   Both sides won the same number of matches.
    B   Eastwick School played sixteen drawn matches.
    C   Southport School was unbeaten fifteen times.
    D   Southport School had the more successful side.
    E   Both sides won a total of eighteen games.

    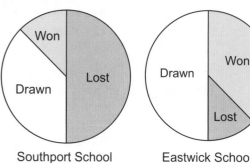

13. A music store recorded the CD sales of three bands in this pictogram.

    How many more CDs did the Victories sell than the Moofs?

Band	CDs Sold
The Victories	◎ ◎ ◎ ◎ ◖
Ebony G	◎ ◎ ◎ ◎
The Moofs	◎ ◎ ◖

    ◎ = 4 CDs

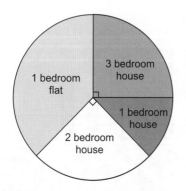

14. This pie chart shows the types of homes 80 people live in.

    How many people live in houses with more than 1 bedroom?

      / 5

Section Four — Data Handling

Mean, Median, Mode and Range

Work out the range of the following sets of numbers.

1. 4, 3, 7, 8, 8

2. 12, 18, 12, 13, 16, 14

3. 5, 9, 22, 6, 4, 17, 12, 9

4. 15, 17, 30, 22, 26, 21, 17, 21

5. 10, 8, 11, 11, 2, 4, 12, 6, 8, 14, 3

/ 5

6. Rajeev sprints for 80 m five times. The time it takes to sprint each 80 m are shown below.

    14 s   11 s   15 s   17 s   12 s   What is his median time?   s

7. In a cricket match, the players in Jo's team scored the following numbers of runs.

    10   15   19   12   20   2   9   31   13   3   17

    What is the median number of runs?

8. The last twelve customers in a shoe shop bought shoes in these sizes.

    4½   8   5½   5   7   7   5½   6½   4   8   7   6

    Which shoe size is the mode?

9. The amount of rainfall measured in Showerham on four separate days is shown below.

    9 mm   12 mm   14 mm   13 mm

    What is the mean rainfall? mm

10. Katie and Vikram are competing in a darts competition.
    Their scores after 3 darts are written on the scoreboard.

    What is the median of
    Katie and Vikram's scores?

Scoreboard			
Dart	1	2	3
Katie:	34	15	20
Vikram:	9	19	12

11. Which of these groups of five numbers have a mean of 10 and a range of 12?
    Circle the correct answer.

    A   12, 14, 13, 11, 12   **C**   8, 27, 19, 17, 4   **E**   16, 4, 9, 7, 14

    B   32, 20, 24, 29, 34   **D**   13, 9, 11, 5, 17

12. Kath rolled a dice 50 times. The table shows how many times she rolled each number.

Number on dice	1	2	3	4	5	6
Frequency	8	12	5	10	7	8

    What is the mode of
    the numbers shown on
    the dice after 50 rolls?

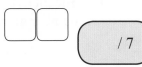

/ 7

Section Four — Data Handling

Probability

Jane plays a game with these three spinners:

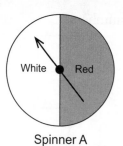

Spinner A

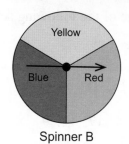

Spinner B

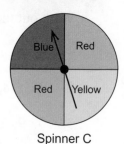

Spinner C

Are each of these statements true or false?
Circle the correct answer.

1. The probability of getting blue on Spinner B is 0.   True   False

2. There is an even chance of getting white or red on Spinner A.   True   False

3. It is equally likely blue, yellow or red could be spun on Spinner C.   True   False

4. The probability of getting yellow on Spinner B is ⅓.   True   False

5. Jane is more likely to get red on Spinner C than Spinner A or B.   True   False

/ 5

6. The labels have come off six tins of soup.
   Harry chooses a tin at random from the ones shown:

   What is the probability of him
   choosing vegetable soup?
   Give your answer as a fraction.

7. A bag contains six balls. One is black, one is yellow and the rest are white.
   Marie picks a ball from the bag at random.

   What is the probability of her picking a white ball? Circle the correct answer.

   A ⁰⁄₆   **B** ⅙   **C** ½   **D** ⅓   **E** ⅔

A teacher has these four number cards. She picks cards at random.

blue   green   green   blue

1   4   5   8

Write down the probability of these events.
Give your answers as fractions.

8. She picks a blue card.

9. She picks a card with a
   number greater than 2.

10. She picks a card that
    is green and even.

11. She picks a card that
    is not both blue and even.

/ 6

Section Four — Data Handling

Angles

This is a diagram of Olly's garden. Use the angles marked in the diagram to answer these questions.

1. Which angle is a right angle?

2. Which angle is biggest?

3. Which two angles are acute angles? and

4. Which angle is an obtuse angle?

5. Which angle is a reflex angle?

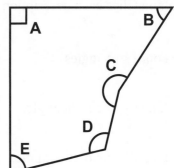

Look at these angles: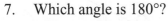

6. Which angle is most likely to be 45°?

7. Which angle is 180°?

8. Which angle is most likely to be 135°?

9. Which angle is most likely to be 70°?

10. Which angle is most likely to be 90°?

/ 10

11. An ant crawls the route shown on the right.
How many times does the ant turn through a right angle?
Circle the correct answer.

    A 0   **B** 1   **C** 2   **D** 3   **E** 4

12. Paul is facing north. He turns clockwise to face west.
What angle does he turn through?

13. Peter is facing south. He turns 90° anticlockwise.
Where is he facing now? Circle the correct answer.

    A north   **B** south   **C** east   **D** west   **E** south-east

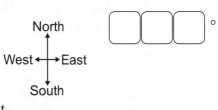

North
West ←→ East
South

14. What is the size of angle *x* between the minute hand and
the hour hand at four o'clock? Circle the correct answer.

    A 90°   **B** 120°   **C** 240°   **D** 180°   **E** 150°

15. Calculate angle *y*.

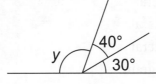

/ 5

2D Shapes

Write down the letter of the shape which matches each description.

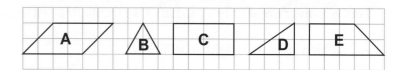

1. Four right angles.

2. Exactly one right angle.

3. Exactly one obtuse angle.

4. Two pairs of parallel sides and no right angles.

5. Three sides and no right angles.

/ 5

Look at the lines on the right. Decide whether each statement is true or false. Circle the correct answer.

6. Line L is parallel to Line M.   true / false

7. Line N is a horizontal line.   true / false

8. Line L is a vertical line.   true / false

9. Line L is parallel to Line O.   true / false

10. Line M is perpendicular to Line N.   true / false

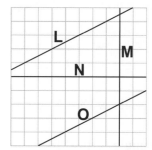

/ 5

11. What is the name of the shape on the right? Circle the correct answer.

    A triangle   **B** octagon   **C** pentagon   **D** hexagon   **E** quadrilateral

12. Which shape below should go in the shaded part of this diagram? Circle the correct answer.

   A   B   C   D   E

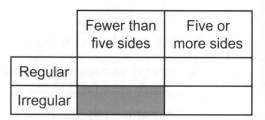

	Fewer than five sides	Five or more sides
Regular		
Irregular		

13. Caley cuts six shapes out of a piece of paper and arranges them to make this picture. Which shapes did she use? Circle the correct answer.

    A   3 pentagons, 2 octagons, 1 rectangle
    B   3 hexagons, 2 octagons, 1 quadrilateral
    C   3 pentagons, 2 octagons, 1 quadrilateral
    D   2 pentagons, 3 octagons, 1 quadrilateral
    E   3 pentagons, 2 octagons, 1 parallelogram

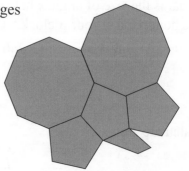

/ 3

2D Shapes

14. Which of these shapes cannot fit together with other identical shapes without leaving any gaps? Circle the correct answer.

A   B   C   D   E

15. Molly is describing a shape. She says, "It has three sides. Only two of the angles are equal."
    What shape is she describing? Circle the correct answer.

    A equilateral triangle   **B** hexagon   **C** pentagon   **D** quadrilateral   **E** isosceles triangle

16. Maryam has a shape. Part of the sorting diagram she uses to identify it is shown on the right.
    Maryam answers 'Yes' to the first two questions.
    Which of the shapes below could she have?
    Circle the correct answer.

    A triangle   **D** parallelogram
    B kite   **E** hexagon
    C pentagon

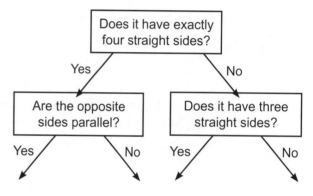

17. Work out the name of this quadrilateral from these clues. Circle the correct answer.
    • It has two pairs of equal length sides.
    • Its sides are not all the same length.
    • The diagonals always cross at right angles.

    A rhombus   **B** kite   **C** parallelogram   **D** rectangle   **E** square

18. Which of these statements about triangles is true? Circle the correct answer.

    A   A triangle can have two right angles.
    B   An equilateral triangle has three acute angles.
    C   A scalene triangle must have an obtuse angle.
    D   The angles in a triangle always add up to 200 degrees.
    E   An isosceles triangle has three equal sides.

19. Look at this Venn diagram. Which shape is in the wrong place?

    Shape [ ]

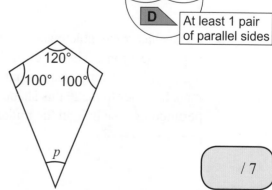

20. The sizes of three of the angles in this kite are given.
    What size is angle p?

    [ ][ ][ ] °

Section Five — Shape and Space

/ 7

2D Shapes — Perimeter and Area

Kate drew four shapes onto squared paper. Each square on the paper has sides of 1 cm.

1. What is the perimeter of shape A? ⬚⬚ cm

The diagrams on this page are not drawn to scale.

2. What is the area of shape B? ⬚⬚ cm²

3. What is the area of shape C? ⬚⬚ cm²

4. What is the area of shape D? ⬚⬚ cm²

5. What is the perimeter of shape C? ⬚⬚ cm

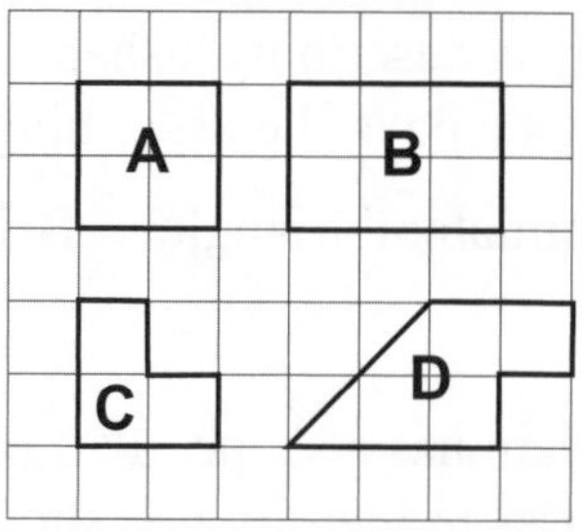

/ 5

6. These five letters are drawn on a 1 cm² grid. Which of these letters does not have an area of 7 cm²? Circle the correct answer.

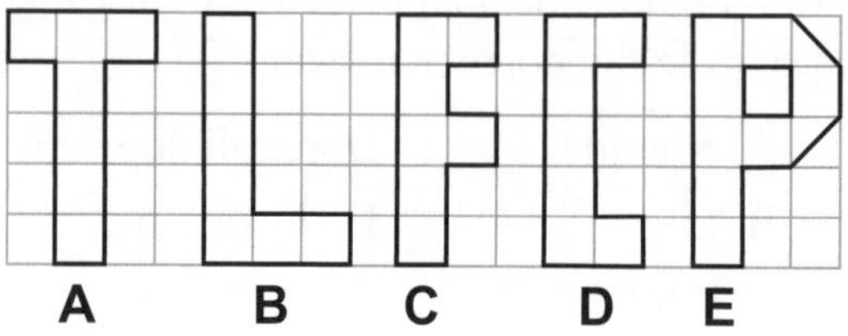

A   B   C   D   E

7. Which two of these shapes have the same area?

⬚ and ⬚

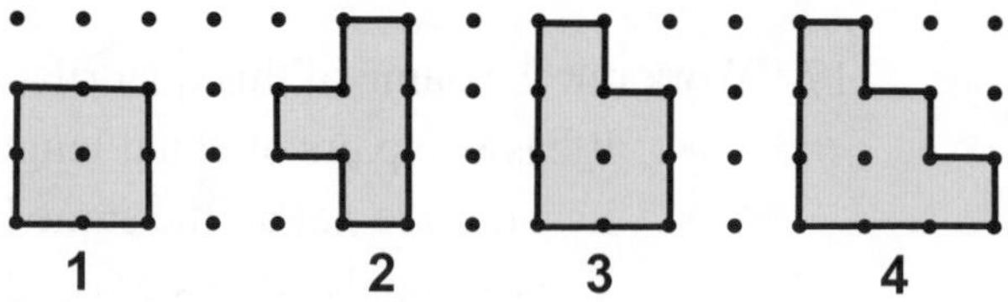

1   2   3   4

The dimensions of three shapes are shown on the right.

8. What is the perimeter of square P? ⬚⬚ cm

9. What is the perimeter of rectangle Q? ⬚⬚ cm

10. What is the area of square P? ⬚⬚ cm²

11. What is the area of rectangle Q? ⬚⬚ cm²

12. Shape R is a regular polygon. What is its perimeter? ⬚⬚ cm

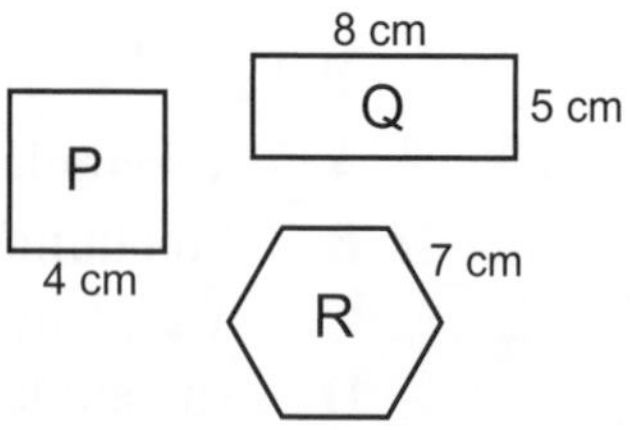

8 cm   Q   5 cm

P   4 cm

R   7 cm

13. Carlos has some table mats in the shape of regular octagons. The edges of the table mats are each 20 cm long. Carlos puts 6 of the table mats together to make this shape. What is the perimeter of the hole in the middle of the shape?

⬚⬚⬚ cm

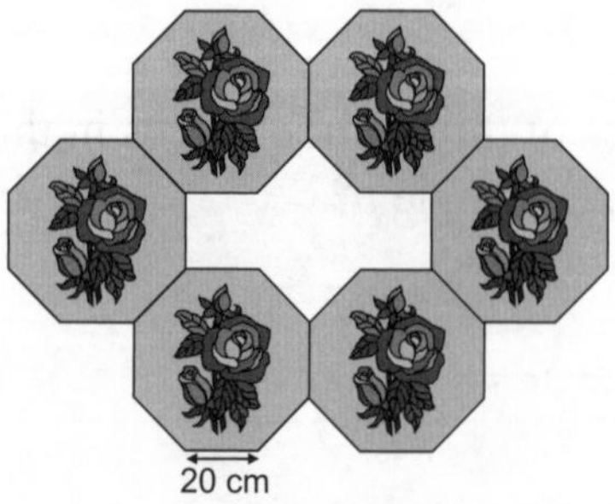

20 cm

/ 8

Section Five — Shape and Space

2D Shapes — Perimeter and Area

14. What is the approximate area of the island shown on this map?
    Each square shows an area of 1 km². Circle the correct answer.

    A 6 km²   **C** 14 km²   **E** 8 km²

    B 10 km²   **D** 12 km²

15. Swimming pool A is rectangular and has an area of 72 m².
    Its width is 6 m. What is its length?   ☐☐ m

16. Swimming pool B is also rectangular and has a perimeter of 90 m.
    Its length is 25 m. What is its width?   ☐☐ m

17. Mr Jones had a rectangular lawn measuring 15 m by 40 m.
    He built a square garage measuring 10 m by 10 m in the
    corner of his lawn. What area of lawn does he have left?

    ☐☐☐ m²

18. Ben is painting this cube. Its edges are 4 cm long.
    What is the total area that he paints?

    ☐☐☐ cm²

    Hint: Don't forget the faces of the cube that you can't see.

19. The diagram shows a rectangular notepad.
    It has a perimeter of 70 cm. What is its width?

    ☐☐ cm

Annie drew the shape on the right and measured some of the side lengths.

20. What is the area of the shape Annie drew?

    ☐☐☐ cm²

21. What is the perimeter of the shape Annie drew?

    ☐☐☐ cm

22. Here is a plan of Abdul's garden. He walks his dog
    around the edge of the garden ten times.
    How much less than one kilometre does he walk?
    Circle the correct answer.

    A 38 m   **B** 62 m   **C** 380 m   **D** 320 m   **E** 620 m

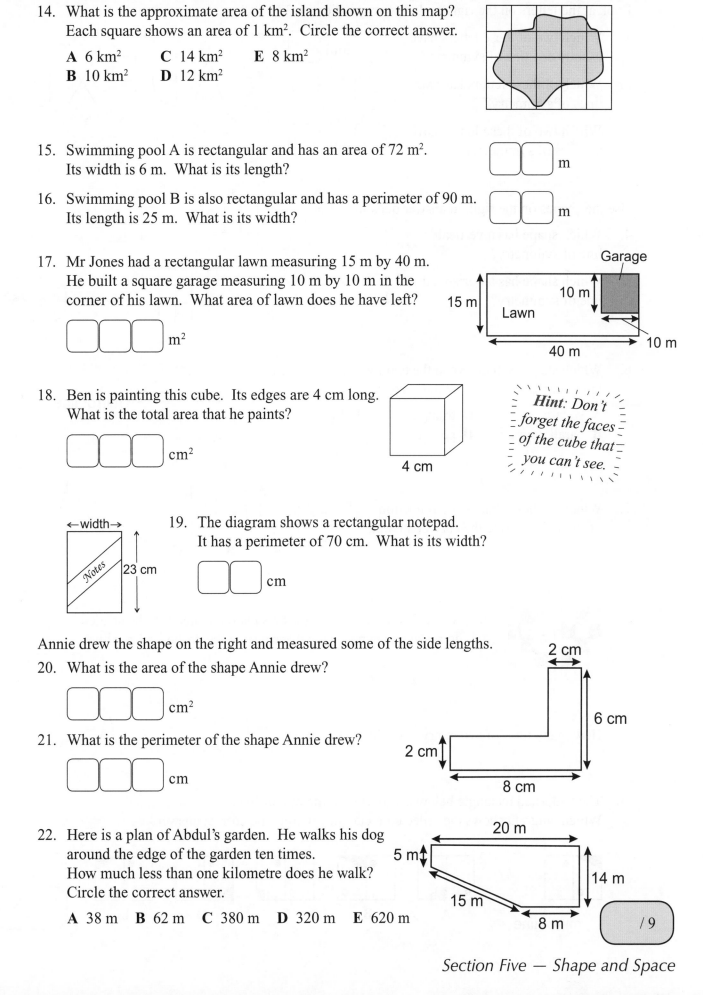

/ 9

Section Five — Shape and Space

Symmetry

Look at the letters on the right and answer questions 1-3.

1. Which two of these letters have exactly one line of symmetry?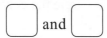

2. Which of these letters has two lines of symmetry?

3. Which two of these letters have no lines of symmetry?

Use the shapes on the right to answer questions 4-5.

4. Which shape has a vertical line of symmetry?

5. Which shape has a horizontal line of symmetry?

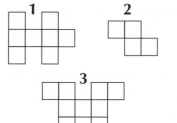

6. Which shape is made when the two lines are reflected in the mirror line? Circle the correct answer.

   A square   **C** triangle   **E** kite
   B parallelogram   **D** pentagon

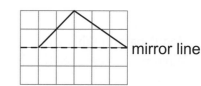

7. Which of these shapes is a reflection of shape P? Circle the correct answer.

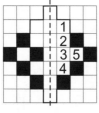

8. Write down the number of the square that needs to be shaded to make a symmetrical pattern across the dashed mirror line.

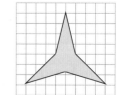

9. How many lines of symmetry does this shape have?

10. The patterned rectangle below is reflected in the mirror line.
    Which diagram shows the reflected rectangle? Circle the correct answer.

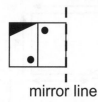

mirror line   **A**   **B**   **C**   **D**   **E**

/ 5

3D Shapes

Look at these 3D shapes. Write the letter for each shape in the correct place in the table.

A   B   C   D   E

	Shape	Number of square or rectangular faces	Number of triangular faces	Number of circular faces
1.		3	2	0
2.		0	0	1
3.		6	0	0
4.		1	4	0
5.		0	4	0

Answer questions 6-10 using shapes A-E above.

6. Which shape has 5 vertices?

7. Which shape has 12 edges?

8. Which shape has one edge and one vertex?

9. Which two shapes are pyramids? [ ] and [ ]

10. Which two shapes are prisms? [ ] and [ ]

/ 10

11. What is the name of this 3D shape? Circle the correct answer.

     A sphere   **B** cylinder   **C** cuboid   **D** cone   **E** cube

12. Which two of these shapes are nets of closed cubes?

[ ] and [ ]

   1   2   3   4   5

13. Which of the following statements is false? Circle the correct answer.

     A   A cylinder has a curved face.   **D**   Half a sphere is called a hemisphere.
     B   A cube has eight vertices.   **E**   All the angles in a cuboid are right-angles.
     C   A cone is a type of triangular prism.

14. This cuboid is made of 1 cm³ blocks. What is its volume?

[ ] [ ] [ ] cm³

/ 4

Section Five — Shape and Space

3D Shapes

15. Which of the shapes below should go in the shaded box in this sorting diagram? Circle the correct answer.

    A   cylinder
    B   cone
    C   triangular prism
    D   sphere
    E   cuboid

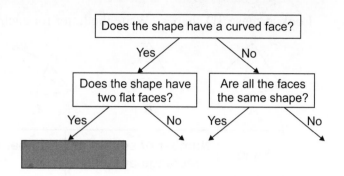

16. How many one centimetre cubes will fit into the cardboard box on the right?

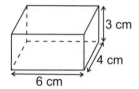

17. What 3D shape can be constructed from this net? Circle the correct answer.

    A cone   C triangular-based pyramid   E triangular prism
    B cube   D square-based pyramid

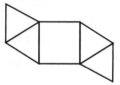

18. The opposite faces of a dice add up to seven. What number should replace X on this net of a dice?

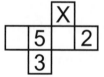

19. Look at this cuboid. One edge is marked by an X. How many edges are parallel to this edge? Circle the correct answer.

    A 1   B 2   C 3   D 5   E 7

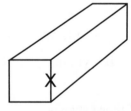

Hint: You can't see all of the edges on this diagram of a cuboid.

20. The cube on the right has shaded triangles on three faces. Which of the following is the net of this cube? Circle the correct answer.

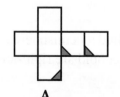

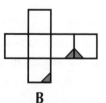

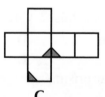

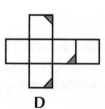

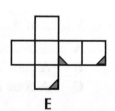

    A   B   C   D   E

21. A cuboid is 4 cm long and 2 cm wide. If it has a volume of 88 cm³, what is its height?

 cm

/ 7

Section Five — Shape and Space

Shape Problems

Look at this piece of card with five holes in it. Gilbert has a card shape, which is labelled P, below.

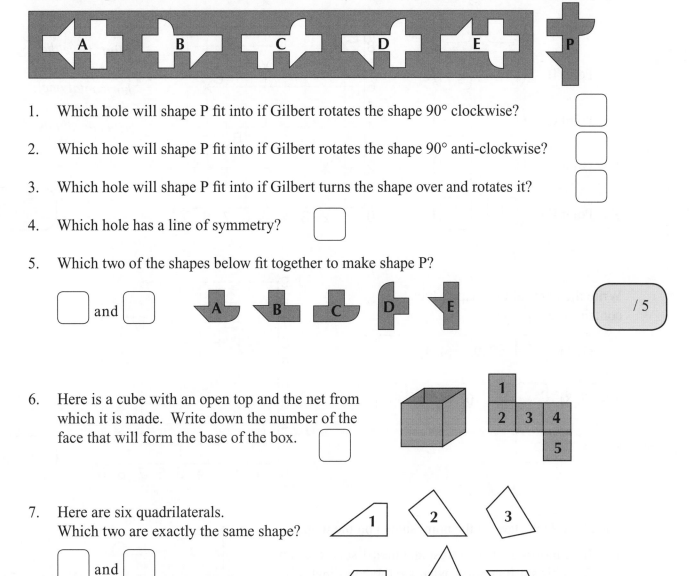

1. Which hole will shape P fit into if Gilbert rotates the shape 90° clockwise?

2. Which hole will shape P fit into if Gilbert rotates the shape 90° anti-clockwise?

3. Which hole will shape P fit into if Gilbert turns the shape over and rotates it?

4. Which hole has a line of symmetry?

5. Which two of the shapes below fit together to make shape P?

   □ and □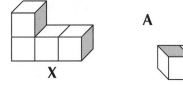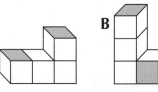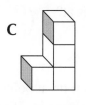

   / 5

6. Here is a cube with an open top and the net from which it is made. Write down the number of the face that will form the base of the box. □

7. Here are six quadrilaterals.
   Which two are exactly the same shape?

   □ and □

8. Ann makes shape X from four cubes. Two faces of the shape are shaded. Which of the options below could be shape X in a different position? Circle the correct answer.

   X   A   B   C   D   E

9. Rosie made shape F using four identical tiles.
   Which of A-E is one of these tiles? Circle the correct answer.

                  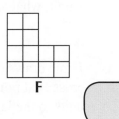

   A   B   C   D   E   F

   / 4

Section Five — Shape and Space

Coordinates

Write the coordinates of each point.

1. Point A (⬜ , ⬜)

2. Point B (⬜ , ⬜)

3. Point C (⬜ , ⬜)

4. Point D (⬜ , ⬜)

5. Point E (⬜ , ⬜)

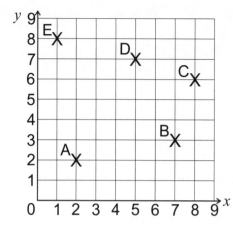

Hint: Give the x-axis value (the horizontal one) first when you write coordinates.

/ 5

Write the letter of the shape which contains these points.

6. (1, 1) ⬜   9. (4, 4) ⬜

7. (7, 8) ⬜   10. (2, 6) ⬜

8. (8, 2) ⬜

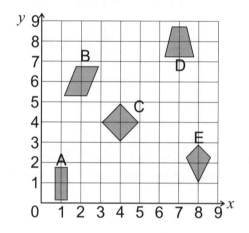

/ 5

Each time Jack starts at the point shown on the map.

11. If he moves 2 squares west and then 1 square south from his starting point, what are the coordinates of the point he finishes at? (⬜ , ⬜)

12. If he moves 2 squares east and then 2 squares north from his starting point, what are the coordinates of the point he finishes at? (⬜ , ⬜)

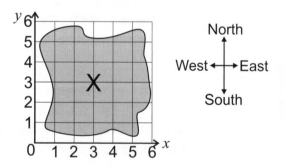

13. Samir puts his pencil tip at point (9, 3) on a grid. He moves it three squares downwards. If each grid square is 1 unit by 1 unit, what are the new coordinates of his pencil tip? (⬜ , ⬜)

14. Jamie draws cross A at point (7, 2) on a grid. He draws cross B at point (2, 5) on the same grid. How many units to the left of cross A is cross B? ⬜ units

/ 4

Section Five — Shape and Space

Coordinates

15. The coordinates of three corners of a rectangle are shown. What are the coordinates of corner A?

   A (2, 1)   **D** (4, 4)
   B (2, 4)   **E** (1, 2)
   C (1, 4)

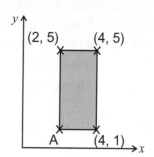

16. Three corners of a rectangle are marked on this grid. What are the coordinates of the rectangle's fourth corner?

$$\left(\boxed{}\, ,\, \boxed{}\right)$$

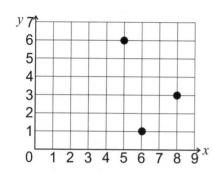

17. Find the coordinates of the midpoint of this line. 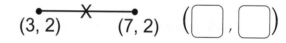 $\left(\boxed{}\, ,\, \boxed{}\right)$

Three corners of a kite are marked on this grid.

18. What could be the coordinates of the kite's fourth corner? Circle the correct answer.

   A (4, 3)   **B** (5, 0)   **C** (2, 5)   **D** (3, 6)   **E** (5, 2)

19. Which of these coordinates would not be inside the kite? Circle the correct answer.

   A (4, 4)   **B** (6, 4)   **C** (2, 2)   **D** (7, 5)   **E** (4, 3)

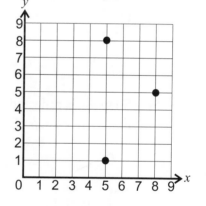

20. What shape is drawn if the points (0, 0), (1, 2), (3, 2) and (2, 0) are joined, in order, by straight lines? Circle the correct answer.

   A square   **D** pentagon
   B rectangle   **E** trapezium
   C parallelogram

Hint: If you can't picture what the shape looks like, try sketching the points on a rough piece of paper.

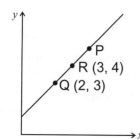

21. The distance between the points Q and R is the same as the distance between points R and P. What are the coordinates of point P?

$$\left(\boxed{}\, ,\, \boxed{}\right)$$

/ 7

Section Five — Shape and Space

Transformations

1. The shape shown on the grid is reflected in the mirror line. What are the coordinates of the reflection of point A? Circle the correct answer.

   A (6, 3)   **B** (6, 2)   **C** (6, 4)   **D** (2, 6)   **E** (5, 3)

2. What are the coordinates of the reflection of point B?

   (☐ , ☐)

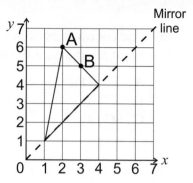

Evie draws a shape G on the grid.

3. If she translates shape G 3 squares right and 5 squares up to give shape H, what will the new coordinates of point Q be?

   (☐ , ☐)

4. Evie translates shape G 2 squares right, 2 squares up and 1 square left to give shape J. What are the new coordinates of point Q?

   (☐ , ☐)

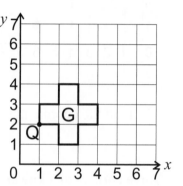

5. Shape R is reflected in a vertical line to give shape S. Shape S is then reflected in a horizontal line to give shape T. Which of these looks like Shape T? Circle the correct answer.

A   **B**   **C**   **D**   **E**

6. The triangle shown on this grid is reflected in the mirror line. What are the coordinates of the reflection of point T?

   (☐ , ☐)

7. The reflected triangle is then translated 1 square right and 2 squares up. What is the difference between the y coordinate of point T and the image of T on the new triangle? Circle the correct answer.

   A 1   **B** 2   **C** 3   **D** 4   **E** 5

/ 7

Section Five — Shape and Space

Units

Choose the most likely unit from the options to replace the question mark in these sentences.
Circle the correct answer.

1. A human weighs 60 ?.   **A** g   **B** m   **C** kg   **D** km

2. A giraffe is about 4.95 ? tall.   **A** cm   **B** m   **C** kg   **D** km

3. A bucket can hold about 18 ? of water.   **A** ml   **B** m   **C** kg   **D** litres

4. A cake contains 125 ? of sugar.   **A** g   **B** cm   **C** kg   **D** m

5. Mount Everest is about 8.8 ? high.   **A** cm   **B** m   **C** litres   **D** km

6. A mug holds about 250 ? of coffee.   **A** km   **B** ml   **C** kg   **D** litres

7. Eve runs a race that is 5 km long.
    How far did she run in metres?   ☐☐☐☐ m

8. David has cycled 900 m. How much further
    does he need to go to reach one km?   ☐☐☐☐ m

9. A caterpillar measures 7.9 cm.
    How long is the caterpillar in millimetres?   ☐☐☐☐ mm

10. A bottle holds 0.5 litres of orange juice.
    How many millilitres is this?   ☐☐☐☐ ml

11. James buys some bags of sweets. Each bag
    weighs 25 g. How many bags will he need   ☐☐☐☐   / 11
    to buy to have 1 kg of sweets?

12. Which of these is the most likely mass of an apple? Circle the correct answer.

    A 1000 g   **B** 150 g   **C** 5 g   **D** 1 g   **E** 10 g

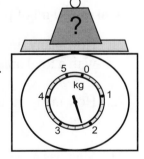

13. What weight is shown on the set of scales? Give your answer in grams.

     g

14. Which of the following statements is unlikely to be true?
    Circle the correct answer.

    A   A walking route is 15 km long.

    B   A dog measures 63 m from his nose to his tail.

    C   A classroom is 9000 mm wide.

    D   A door is 195 cm high.

    E   An exercise book has a width of 180 mm.

Hint: Make sure you look at the units as well as the number when you're deciding if each option sounds sensible.

/ 3

Units

15. Zeke wants to measure the volume of milk he puts on his cereal.
    What would be the most sensible units to use? Circle the correct answer.
    A g   **B** ml   **C** kg   **D** m   **E** mm

16. Anita has a 0.5 kg bar of chocolate. If she eats 10 g of it,
    how many grams of chocolate does she have left?

    ☐☐☐☐ g

17. A glass holds 250 ml. How many glassfuls could you
    pour from a 1½ litre bottle of lemonade?

    ☐☐☐

18. Which of these is equal to 1500? Circle the correct answer.
    A   The number of millilitres in 15 litres.
    B   The number of millimetres in 150 centimetres.
    C   The number of metres in 0.15 kilometres.
    D   The number of grams in 150 kilograms.
    E   The number of centimetres in 1.5 metres

19. A plan has been drawn using the scale 1 cm = 50 cm.
    What would be the real length of a line drawn
    8 cm long on the plan in metres?

    ☐☐☐☐ m

20. Adam bakes a fruit cake that weighs 1 kg. He cuts away a section that weighs 50 g.
    Which diagram best shows the amount of cake that would be left? Circle the correct answer.

    A   **B**   **C**   **D**   **E**

It takes 250 ml of paint to cover 1 m² of wall. Each tin holds 1 litre of paint.

21. How many tins will be needed to paint a wall
    with a total area of 12 m²?

    ☐☐

22. How many m² of wall would 5 tins of paint cover?

    ☐☐☐ m²

23. Matt has a piece of string that is 120 mm long. Kim has a
    piece of string that is 0.1 m long. How much longer is Matt's
    piece of string than Kim's piece of string in centimetres?

    ☐☐ cm

24. A box containing 50 books weighs 15.5 kg.
    When the box is empty it weighs 500 g.
    How much does each book weigh?

    ☐☐☐☐ g

    / 10

Section Six — Units and Measures

Time

A   B   C   D

1. Kevin started travelling to his friend's house at the time shown on clock A. What time did Kevin set off?

    ☐☐ : ☐☐

2. Kevin was on the bus between the times shown on clocks B and C. How long was the bus journey?

    ☐☐ minutes

3. Kevin got on a train at the time shown on clock D. The train journey was 45 minutes long. What time did he get off the train?

    ☐☐ : ☐☐   / 3

The times shown below are all in the 24-hour clock.

20:25	05:25	17:25	15:25	12:15
A	B	C	D	E

4. Which clock shows a time in the morning? ☐

6. Which clock shows the time as twenty five past three? ☐

5. Which clock shows the latest time? ☐

7. Which clock shows the time as 5:25 pm? ☐

8. What is the difference in the times shown by clocks D and E?

    ☐☐ hours ☐☐ minutes   / 5

9. Circle the time below that is the same as 22:17.

    A 2:17 am   **B** 12:17 pm   **C** 10:17 am   **D** 10:17 pm   **E** 12:17 am

This is a train timetable for trains between Southwold and Westerton.

	Train A	Train B	Train C	Train D	Train E
Southwold	08:30	09:45	10:20	11:05	12:00
Eastford	08:45	10:10		11:30	
Northover	09:33	10:27	11:25	12:12	13:24
Westerton	10:00	11:15	12:11	12:47	13:58

10. If Amy leaves Eastford at 10:10, what time will she get to Westerton?   ☐☐ : ☐☐

11. What is the latest time that Sam could leave Southwold in order to be in time for an appointment in Northover at 12 noon?   ☐☐ : ☐☐

12. How many days are there in total during March, April, May and June?   ☐☐☐☐ days   / 4

Section Six — Units and Measures

Time

13. Jane and Susan are identical twins. Jane was born at 8:15 am and Susan was born at 8:55 am. How many minutes older than Susan is Jane? ⬚⬚ minutes

14. The table shows the start times of several television programmes. If you got home at 9:25 am, how long would you have to wait until Cartoons started?

⬚⬚ minutes

6:30	Breakfast Time
7:15	What's Happening
7:30	News
7:50	Learn with Ted
10:10	Cartoons

15. In 2011, January 9th was on a Sunday. What day of the week was January 26th in that year? Circle the correct answer.

A Monday   B Tuesday   C Wednesday   D Thursday   E Friday   F Saturday   G Sunday

16. A train was due to reach Preston at 4:25 am but it was one and three quarter hours late. What time did it arrive? ⬚⬚:⬚⬚ am

17. Anita makes a New Year's resolution to eat an apple every day. If she starts on the 1st January, in what month will she eat the hundredth apple? Circle the correct answer.

A February   B March   C April   D May   E June

18. If it is 14:10, what time was it thirty-five minutes ago? ⬚⬚:⬚⬚

19. If it is 23:58, what time will it be in fifteen minutes? ⬚⬚:⬚⬚

20. Sarah's birthday is on the 12th of June. On the 21st of May, how many days is it until Sarah's birthday? ⬚⬚ days

21. Johnny went to sleep at 10:15 pm. He woke up the next day at 7:30 am. How long did he sleep for? ⬚⬚ hours ⬚⬚ minutes

22. A film at the Astro Cinema starts at five to eight in the evening. It lasts for 1 hour 35 minutes. What time does the film finish? Give your answer using the 24-hour clock. ⬚⬚:⬚⬚

23. The table shows the times letters are collected from a post box. Anja posts a letter at 2:30 pm on Thursday. How long will it be before the letter is collected from the box? ⬚⬚ hours ⬚⬚ minutes

| Monday to Friday | Saturday | Sunday |
| 7 am 1 pm 2 pm | 12:00 noon | No collection |

24. These stopwatches show the times that Don and Ivor ran in a marathon. How much longer did Ivor take than Don? ⬚⬚ minutes ⬚⬚ seconds

Don 2:29:53   Ivor 2:47:01

/ 12

Section Six — Units and Measures

Mixed Problems

1. Annie works from 9 am to 3 pm each day for 5 days. She is paid £210 in total. How much money does she earn each hour?

£ ☐☐.☐☐

2. Suzy's friends' heights are shown in the table. She adds their three heights together and then rounds this to the nearest 10. What number is Suzy left with?

Friend	Height (cm)
Emma	148
Mark	167
Simon	150

☐☐☐ cm

A container can hold 8 litres of water. The empty container is placed under a dripping tap that adds 5 ml of water to the container every second.

3. How many seconds will it take to half-fill the container?

☐☐☐☐ seconds

4. If the tap dripped for 20 minutes, how many litres of water would be in the container?

☐☐☐ litres

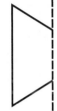

5. Azhar drew half of a shape and reflected it in the mirror line to make a whole shape. What is the name of the whole shape? Circle the correct answer.

A quadrilateral   C triangle   E hexagon
B heptagon   D pentagon

6. Phil records the times he started and finished doing his homework over 3 days. What is the mean time Phil spends doing his homework each day?

☐☐☐ minutes

Day	Start Time	Finish Time
Monday	4:15 pm	5:15 pm
Tuesday	5:05 pm	5:55 pm
Wednesday	5:30 pm	6:10 pm

The temperature in a greenhouse is 14 °C.
A heater is switched on and the temperature in the greenhouse rises by 1 °C every 12 minutes.

7. How long, in hours and minutes, will it take for the temperature in the greenhouse to reach 25 °C?

☐☐ hours ☐☐ minutes

8. What temperature will the greenhouse reach after 3 hours and 24 minutes?

☐☐☐ °C

9. A group of children take part in a 60-hour computer games challenge. If they start at 10:00 am on Friday, when will they finish? Circle the correct answer.

A 10:00 pm on Sunday   D 10:00 am on Monday
B 4:00 pm on Sunday   E 10:00 am on Sunday
C 11:00 pm on Saturday

/ 9

Mixed Problems

10. Four people go on a camping trip. They are charged 60p for each litre of water that they collect. Each person collects 2 litres of water every morning for the five days they are there. How much will they pay for the water altogether? Circle the correct answer.

    A £6   **B** £240   **C** £16   **D** £24   **E** £90

11. Which of the following is the correct expression for the perimeter of this isosceles triangle? Circle the correct answer.

    A $a \times b \times c$ **C** $2a + c$ **E** $2b + 2c$

    B $a \times b + c$ **D** $a + 2c$

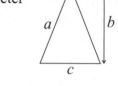

12. Carlo arranges 10 square chocolate brownies on a rectangular board as shown. Each brownie has 8 cm sides. He leaves a 4 cm border around the edge of the brownies. What is the length of the board that he uses?

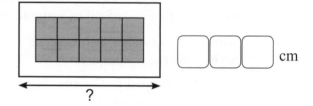

cm

Each child pays £155 to go on a school trip to the Lake District.

13. 20% of each child's payment is used to buy food. How much of each child's payment is not used to buy food?

    £ ⬚⬚⬚.⬚⬚

14. $\frac{3}{5}$ of the payment goes towards the activities they'll do. How much more money goes towards activities than food?

    £ ⬚⬚⬚.⬚⬚

15. Xavi is painting a rectangular wall. The wall is 4 metres long and 2.5 metres high. Xavi has painted 0.5 m² of the wall. What percentage of the wall has he painted?

    ⬚⬚⬚ %

Hanna throws a pair of dice six times. She records the numbers that she rolls in the table. Hanna adds the two numbers together to find her score for each throw.

Throw	1	2	3	4	5	6
Numbers rolled	2 and 3	6 and 1	5 and 1	4 and 5	3 and 6	?

16. If her mean score is 7, what was her score in throw 6?

    ⬚⬚

17. If she rolled two sixes in throw 6, what would her mean score be?

    ⬚⬚

18. There are 32 children in Class 5S. The bar chart shows the number of children who have their birthday each month.

    The bar for March has not been drawn yet. What fraction of the class have their birthday in March? Circle the correct answer.

    A $\frac{1}{6}$ **B** $\frac{1}{8}$ **C** $\frac{4}{16}$ **D** $\frac{2}{5}$ **E** $\frac{1}{4}$

    / 9

Mixed Problems

Chris is making a pasta dish. The recipe says that to make the dish for 4 people, he will need 220 g dried pasta and 150 g cheese.

19. Chris invites 5 friends for dinner. If he wants to make enough pasta for his friends and himself to eat, how much dried pasta will he need?  g

20. There are two types of cheese that make up the amount of cheese in the recipe — cheddar cheese and mozzarella cheese. They are split in the ratio 3:2. If Claire uses the recipe to make the pasta dish for 8 people, how much cheddar cheese will she need?  g

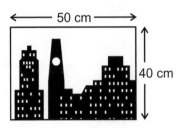

Isobel has bought this painting. It is 50 cm wide and 40 cm tall.

21. What is the area of the painting?  cm²

22. Isobel wants to get the painting framed. She'd like a 5 cm border left around the painting. What would the perimeter of the frame be?  cm

23. Benji cycles 20 km/h. If he cycles for four and a half hours, how many kilometres further would he need to go to complete 100 km?  km

Mark wins £1000 in a photography competition.

24. He gives 5% of the money to charity, $\frac{1}{10}$ to his friend, and he spends the rest on a new camera. How much does his new camera cost? £

25. In the camera shop, there is a camera accessory sale, offering a 25% reduction on each item. If Mark buys a camera bag which was originally £48, a tripod which was £72 and a memory card which was £24, how much money will he save? £

26. It takes two builders 24 days to build one house. How many days would it take six builders to build two houses if they worked at the same speed? Circle the correct answer.
    A 8 days   **B** 24 days   **C** 12 days   **D** 18 days   **E** 16 days

27. Sally's hen lays 1 egg every 3 days. Lydia's hen lays 2 eggs every 5 days. How many more eggs did Lydia's hen lay in April than Sally's hen? ☐☐ eggs

Sophie is making beaded bracelets. This is a table of prices for beads. Packs cannot be split.

Colour	Number in pack	Price
blue	100	£3.20
red	75	£2.90
white	50	£2.85
green	75	£3.05

28. Sophie wants to make 15 bracelets. Each bracelet uses 10 of each colour bead. How much will it cost Sophie to make the 15 bracelets?

£ ☐☐.☐☐

/ 10

Section Seven — Mixed Problems

Assessment Test 1

The rest of the book contains five assessment tests to help you improve your maths skills.

Each test is divided into two parts. Section A is the 'quick maths' section — the questions here are more straightforward but with less time available per question. Section B is the 'long maths' section, the questions are more complex, but there's more time to answer them.

For each test, allow 9 minutes to do Section A and 20 minutes to do Section B.
Work as quickly and as carefully as you can.

You can print **multiple-choice answer sheets** for these questions from our website — go to www.cgplearning.co.uk/11+. If you'd prefer to answer them in write-in format, either write your answers in the spaces provided or circle the **correct answer** from the options given.

Section A — Quick Maths
You have **9 minutes** to complete this section.
There are **25 questions** in this section.

---

1. The length of a large ship is 0.13 km, how long is this in metres?   metres

2. A vegetable patch is in the shape of the rectangle shown on the right. How many lines of symmetry does the vegetable patch have?

3. Sixteen thousand and twenty six people attended a concert. What is this in figures?

   A   1 600 026   C   16 260   E   16 026
   B   1626   D   1 600 206

4. The lowest night time temperature was 26 °C colder than the highest daytime temperature of 18 °C. What was the coldest night time temperature?   –   °C

5. What is the ratio of shaded to non-shaded sections in the shape on the right?

           :

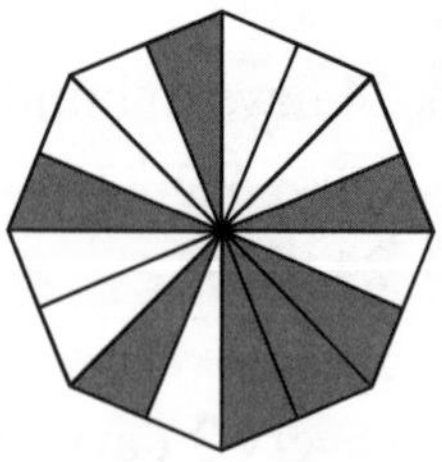

6. Jamila has two hundred and one beads. She gives away 66. How many does she have left?

7. Laura recorded the temperature at 5 times during the night. Which temperature was lowest?

   A   3.32 °C   B   3.8 °C   C   3.12 °C   D   3.08 °C   E   3.2 °C

8. How many 5p coins would be needed to make £3.35?

Carry on to the next question → →

9. What is the weight of the grapes on the scale?

   A 1.53 kg   **C** 1.75 kg   **E** 1.7 kg
   B 1.65 kg   **D** 1.6 kg

10. How many prime numbers are there between ten and thirty?

11. Dana thinks of a number that is a multiple of 7.
    Which of these can't be the number she is thinking of?

    A 550   **B** 210   **C** 49   **D** 21   **E** 77

12. In a bag of assorted mints, 1 in every 8 are spearmint flavour.
    There are 104 mints in the bag, how many are spearmint flavour?

13. Every hour, Charles measures the amount of rain that
    has collected in a bucket in his back garden. His results
    for the first 8 hours are shown on the line graph.
    How much water was there in the bucket after 6 hours?

    ___ ml

14. A class draws a bar chart showing the number of leaves
    on some pea plants they are growing.
    What is the modal number of leaves?

15. $64 \times 1322 = 84\,608$ What is 32×1322?

    A 21 152   **B** 42 304   **C** 28 202   **D** 169 216   **E** 9562

16. $\frac{3}{8}$ of the DVDs in Tara's collection are animated.
    There are 32 DVDs in her collection, how many are animated?

    A 18   **B** 16   **C** 12   **D** 85   **E** 4

17. What is the order of rotational
    symmetry of this shape?

18. $60.837 \times$ ___ $= 6083.7$

19. Katie writes down the following sequence.
    What is the next number in the sequence?

    35   28   21   14

Carry on to the next question →→

20. Heather's train arrives at the time shown on the clock.
    What would the train's arrival time be on a 24-hour clock?

    ☐☐ : ☐☐

21. Joe wants to buy some shoes that normally cost £45. They are in a sale with 10% off.
    How much money off would Joe get if he bought the shoes in the sale?

    £ ☐☐.☐

22. Chen wants to measure the length of a pencil.
    Which of these units would be the most sensible to use?

    A m   **B** km   **C** g   **D** cm   **E** ml

23. Rebecca is buying some bookmarks for her book club.
    Bookmarks cost 60p each and Rebecca has £8.
    How many bookmarks can she buy?

    ☐☐☐

24. Karen has 240 comic books. She gives one third of them to her little sister.
    How many did she give to her little sister?

    A 70   **B** 80   **C** 90   **D** 160   **E** 240

25. All the edges of a cube add to a total length of 48 cm.
    What is the length of one edge of the cube?

    A 12 cm   **B** 4 cm   **C** 5 cm   **D** 4.8 cm   **E** 7 cm   / 25

Section B — Long Maths

You have **20 minutes** to complete this section.
There are **23 questions** in this section.

A drawer contains gel pens and crayons. This table shows how many of each type and colour there are.
Peter closes his eyes and picks one at random.

1. Which of these statements is true?

    A Peter is more likely to pick out a gel pen than a crayon.
    B Peter is twice as likely to pick a blue colour as yellow.
    C Peter is equally likely to pick a red or a green colour.
    D Peter is more likely to pick a green gel pen than a red gel pen.
    E Peter is less likely to pick a blue gel pen than a green crayon.

Colour	Gel Pens	Crayons
Red	7	4
Blue	8	8
Green	5	4
Yellow	1	7

2. What is the probability that Peter will pick a red colour?
   Give your answer as a decimal.

   ☐.☐☐

3. It takes 120 cm of wool to make a friendship bracelet. Two Year 4
   classes are making friendship bracelets. Each class has 25 children.
   How much wool, in metres, will be needed for all Year 4 children
   to make one bracelet each?

   ☐☐☐ m

Carry on to the next question → →

Josie is building a sequence of towers of blocks.
The first 3 towers in her sequence
are shown on the right.

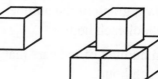
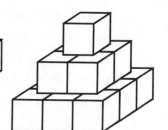

4. How many more blocks will Josie
    need to add to the 3rd tower to make
    the 4th tower in the sequence?

5. How many blocks does Josie need to add to the previous tower,
    in order to make a tower that was n layers high?

    A $n \div n$ **B** $n \times n$ **C** $2n + 1$ **D** $2(n \times n)$ **E** $2(n + 1)$

6. How many blocks, in total, will there be in the 5th tower of the sequence?

The grid on the right shows a triangle with one of the
corners labelled as point C.

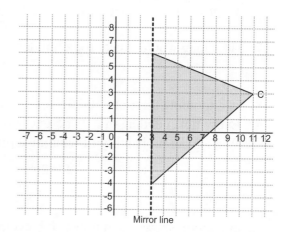

7. What are the coordinates of point C
    of the triangle shown on the grid?

    $\left(\boxed{} , \boxed{} \right)$

8. The triangle is translated up 2 squares.
    What are the new coordinates of point C?

    $\left(\boxed{} , \boxed{} \right)$

9. The original triangle is reflected in the mirror line.
    What are the coordinates of the image of point C?

    A $(3, 3)$ **B** $(-5, 3)$ **C** $(-5, 5)$ **D** $(5, -3)$ **E** $(-3, 3)$

10. Richard gets paid £5.20 per hour for gardening and £4.80 per hour for cleaning.
    One day, Richard spent 3 hours gardening and 4 ½ hours cleaning.
    Which of these calculations gives the total amount Richard was paid?

    A £5.00 × 3 + 60p + 4 × £4.80 + £2.40   **D** £4.80 × 4 − 20p + 5 × £5.20 − £2.60

    B £5.00 × 3 − 60p + 4 × £4.80 − 2.40   **E** £2.40 × 4 + £4.80 + 3 × £5.20

    C £4.80 × 3 + 20p + 4.5 × £5.20

The mass of a biscuit is 25 g and 20% of each biscuit is fat.

11. Charlie eats 3 biscuits. What mass of fat did Charlie eat?

 g

12. Charlie then eats another two biscuits.
    What mass of fat has he now eaten in total?

 g

13. By eating the same biscuits, Jane ate 32.5 g of fat.
    How many biscuits did she eat?

Carry on to the next question →→

Assessment Test 1

A group of children drew a graph of the number of red cars that passed their school each hour.

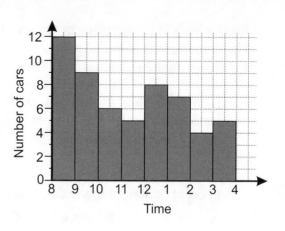

14. What was the mean number of red cars that passed the school each hour?

   A 6   **B** 5   **C** 8   **D** 9   **E** 7

15. How many more red cars drove past between 12 and 2 o'clock than between 2 and 4 o'clock?

   A 6   **B** 5   **C** 8   **D** 9   **E** 7

The amount of time it takes a builder to build a wall (in minutes) is calculated by taking the number of bricks he is using (n), multiplying that by 2 and then adding 1.

16. Which expression gives the amount of time it takes to build a wall?

   A $2(n + 1)$ **B** $n \times n$ **C** $2(n \times n)$ **D** $2n + 1$ **E** $2(n + n)$

17. How long would it take for a builder to build a wall with 56 bricks?

   ☐☐☐ minutes

18. In a tombola there are 100 tickets numbered 001 to 100.
    Every ticket ending in a 0 or 5 gets a prize.
    What is the probability of winning a prize with one ticket?

   A $\frac{1}{50}$ **B** $\frac{1}{2}$ **C** 20%   **D** 40%   **E** $\frac{2}{5}$

The pictogram shows the number of bicycles of each colour in the school bike shed.

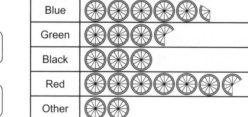

19. How many bicycles are there altogether?

   ☐☐☐

20. How many more red bicycles are there than blue bicycles?

   ☐☐☐

21. A rectangular yard is 0.2 m long and 7 m wide. What volume of concrete is needed to cover the yard with a concrete layer one tenth of a metre thick?

   A 104 m³   **B** 14 m³   **C** 1.4 m³   **D** 0.14 m³   **E** 0.014 m³

22. Chen has cut the first slice of this cake.
    All the other slices will be the same size.
    How many slices will there be altogether?

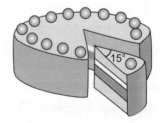

   ☐☐☐

23. A school is preparing for a trip. One adult is needed to look after each group of six children.
    One coach has 42 seats. 162 children have paid for the trip.

    How many coaches will be needed?

   ☐☐   / 23

Assessment Test 2

Allow 9 minutes to do Section A and 20 minutes to do Section B.
Work as quickly and as carefully as you can.

You can print **multiple-choice answer sheets** for these questions from our website — go to
www.cgplearning.co.uk/11+. If you'd prefer to answer them in write-in format, either write
your answers in the spaces provided or circle the **correct answer** from the options given.

Section A — Quick Maths
You have **9 minutes** to complete this section.
There are **25 questions** in this section.

1. There were fifty three thousand and twenty four supporters
    at a football match. Write this number in figures.

2. A school designed three possible shapes for the new playground
    (shown on the right). What type of polygon are they?

    A pentagon   **C** quadrilateral   **E** heptagon

    B octagon   **D** hexagon

3. Which of these is the best estimate of the weight of a horse?

    A 40 g   **B** 40 kg   **C** 4 g   **D** 400 kg   **E** 400 g

4. Karen writes the following sequence. What is the next number in this sequence?

    145   146   148   151   155

5. One Saturday, the temperature in Quebec was −16 °C and the temperature in England was 5 °C.

    What was the temperature difference between Quebec and England?   °C

6. $24 \times 4 = 96$ What is 24×400?

7. Chunni measured the distance round the outside of her bicycle wheel.
    Which of these is most likely to be the length Chunni measured?

    A 1.70 cm   **B** 17 cm   **C** 17 m   **D** 170000 mm   **E** 1.7 m

8. 378 fish were divided equally between 9 fish tanks.
    How many fish were put in each tank?

9. Janet has drawn the following diagram.

    What is the size of angle k?   °

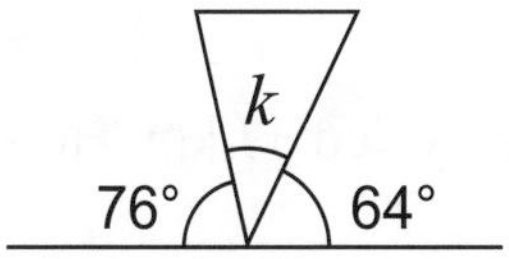

    76°   64°

10. The distance from Flipperton to Cronstone is 872.63 miles.

    What is this distance rounded to the nearest tenth of a mile?   .   miles

Carry on to the next question →→

11. The ages of Hannah's closest relatives are: 10, 25, 30, 40, 45, 55 and 75.
    Which three of her relative's ages add up to 100?

    A   25, 55, 30   **B**   55, 10, 30   **C**   45, 40, 10   **D**   45, 30, 25   **E**   75, 10, 25

12. Mel is trying to work out which corner of her room to put a desk in.
    The shape of her room is shown on the right.
    Which angle is closest to a right angle?

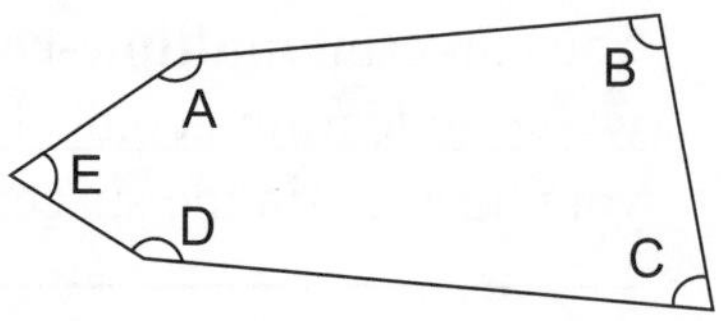

    A   **B**   **C**   **D**   **E**

13. A 200 g bag of mixed nuts contains 25% peanuts.
    How many grams of peanuts are in the bag?   ☐☐☐ g

14. The cost of a phone call is £1.50 plus 20p for every minute the phone call lasts.

    How much would a phone call cost if it lasted 7 minutes?   £ ☐.☐☐

15. The tallest living person is about $17\frac{1}{2}$ feet. What is this as a decimal?   ☐☐.☐ feet

16. How much change would you receive from a £10 note
    if you bought a sack of potatoes for £5.73?   £ ☐.☐☐

17. Gemma looks at her alarm clock at each time shown below. Which time is closest to midnight?

    | 00:35 | | 01:02 | | 22:55 | | 23:35 | | 00:55 |
    | **A** | | **B** | | **C** | | **D** | | **E** |

18. Helga is working out how symmetrical the letters in her name are.

    How many lines of symmetry does the letter H have?   ☐

19. The table below shows the number of pictures on each page of a children's story book.

Number of pictures	2	3	4	5	6
Number of pages	9	6	14	9	21

    What is the modal number
    of pictures on a page?   ☐☐

20. Barney finishes a race in 13.8 seconds. Brenda finishes 1.723 seconds after him.

    How long did Brenda take to finish the race?   ☐☐.☐☐☐ seconds

21. Mark cycled 37 km. How far is this in metres?   ☐☐☐☐☐ metres

22. Alan has two sisters, one is 3 years old and the other is 5 years old.
    Which of the following is a common multiple of their ages?

    A   12   **B**   45   **C**   25   **D**   28   **E**   50

Carry on to the next question →→

Assessment Test 2

23. Mrs Jones uses the calculation 220 ÷ (37 − 26) to work out how many pupils should be in each geography class. What is the answer?

☐☐ pupils

24. A car can travel 8.5 miles per litre of fuel. How many miles can it travel on 40 litres of fuel?

☐☐☐ miles

25. Tom rides his bike twice as far as his brother, Lewis. Lewis rode Y miles.

How far did both of them ride altogether ?

A 2Y   B 1 + 2Y   C Y × Y + 1   D 1.5Y   E 3Y

/ 25

Section B — Long Maths

You have **20 minutes** to complete this section.
There are **23 questions** in this section.

---

1. Brian and two friends divide some sweets equally amongst themselves.
Which of these numbers could be the total number of sweets?

A 334   B 101   C 227   D 211   E 177

The table below shows the cost of postage for items of different weights.

2. Mark has two parcels to post, one weighs 180 g and the other weighs 90 g. What is the minimum amount that Mark could pay to post his parcels?

£ ☐.☐☐

Weight	Postage cost	
	1st Class	2nd Class
Up to 100 g	90p	69p
100 – 250 g	120p	110p
251 – 500 g	160p	140p
Over 500 g	230p	190p

3. If Mark bundled both of his parcels together and posted it as one parcel, how much could he save?

£ ☐.☐☐

The following Venn diagram is used to show the common factors of 24 and 108.

4. Which of these numbers can be placed into the shaded area of this Venn diagram?

A 8   B 10   C 12   D 14   E 16

5. How many numbers between 0 and 10 would appear in the shaded area of this Venn diagram?

A 1   B 2   C 3   D 4   E 5

6. The pie chart shows how many children wear full uniform, part of the uniform or no uniform at a school.

What fraction of the total number of children wear full school uniform?

A ¼   B ½   C ¾   D ⅙   E ⅓

Carry on to the next question →→

Assessment Test 2

7. The diagram on the right shows the first 3 hexagons in a sequence.
   The hexagons are all regular.

   What is the perimeter of the
   6th hexagon in the sequence? ◻◻ cm

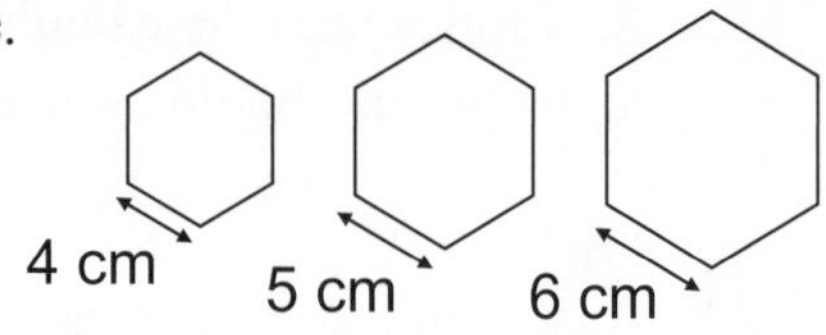

   4 cm   5 cm   6 cm

On five consecutive days the amount of time it rained was rounded
to the nearest hour and recorded in the pictogram below.

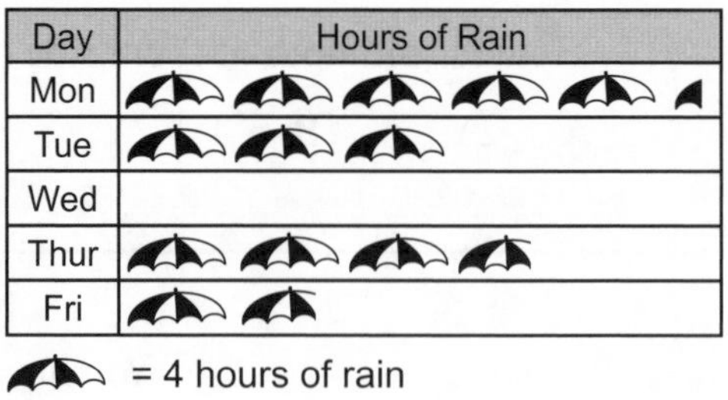

Day	Hours of Rain
Mon	🌂🌂🌂🌂🌂☂
Tue	🌂🌂🌂
Wed	
Thur	🌂🌂🌂🌂
Fri	🌂🌂

🌂 = 4 hours of rain

8. How many more hours of rain were
   there on Monday than on Thursday? ◻◻ hours

9. What was the mean number
   of hours of rain per day? ◻◻ hours

Reiko is making flapjacks. Three flapjacks take 90 g of sugar.

10. How many flapjacks could Reiko make with 540 g of sugar? ◻◻

11. Reiko has a 2 kg bag of sugar.
    How much sugar would she have left if she made 33 flapjacks? ◻◻◻◻ g

12. Reiko actually needs to make 25 flapjacks.
    How much sugar will she use? ◻◻◻◻ g

13. A fair dice with the numbers 1 to 6 is rolled. Which of these statements is true?

    A   The probability of rolling either a 2 or 4 is the same as the probability of getting a 6.
    B   The probability of rolling an odd number is greater than that of getting an even number.
    C   The probability of rolling a number less than four is the same as getting a four.
    D   The probability of rolling a five or a six is the same as getting a one or a two.
    E   The probability of rolling an odd number is less than that of getting an even number.

14. Three corners of a parallelogram
    have been marked on this grid.

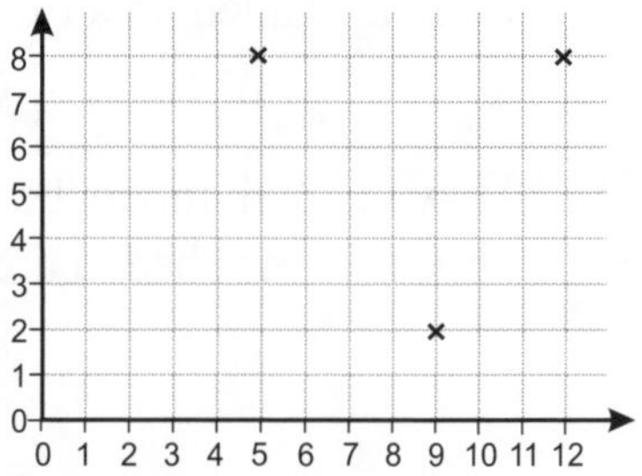

    Which of these could be the coordinates of the fourth corner?

    A   (2, 3)   C   (3, 2)   E   (4, 2)
    B   (2, 2)   D   (1, 1)

15. Sanji is selling ice creams and needs to buy thirty ice cream cones.
    He can buy normal cones or waffle cones.

    Waffle cone: 46p each
    Normal cone: 36p each

    How much more would it cost him
    to buy waffle cones instead of normal cones?   £ ◻.◻◻

Carry on to the next question →→

16. Joe rings 26 friends to invite them to his party. Phone calls cost 12p a minute to a landline and 25p a minute to a mobile phone. He rings 16 of his friends on their mobile phones and 10 of his friends on their landlines. Each phone call lasts for 2 minutes.

How much will it cost him to phone all 26 friends?

 £ ⬚ ⬚ . ⬚ ⬚

This tally chart and bar chart show the number of different types of flowers in a flower bed. The data for one type of flower has not been drawn on the bar chart.

Flower	Tally	Total
Daisies	JHT JHT JHT JHT JHT JHT	30
Buttercups	JHT JHT JHT JHT II	22
Dandelions	JHT JHT JHT	15
Stitchwort	JHT JHT JHT II	17
Chickweed	JHT JHT JHT JHT JHT JHT JHT I	36

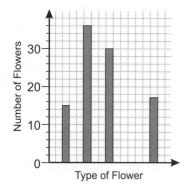

17. How many more chickweed were there than stitchwort and dandelions combined?

⬚ ⬚

18. Which type of flower is missing from the bar chart?

A Daisies   **B** Buttercups   **C** Dandelions   **D** Stitchwort   **E** Chickweed

19. What proportion of the flowers were daisies? Simplify your answer.

⬚ ⬚ in every ⬚ ⬚ ⬚

20. This shape is made from four identical rectangles each measuring 8 cm by 2 cm.

What is the perimeter of this shape?

⬚ ⬚ cm

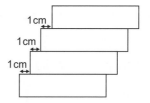

This line graph shows how the temperature changed during one week.

21. What was the temperature range over the week?

⬚ ⬚ °C

22. What was the median temperature for the week?

⬚ ⬚ °C

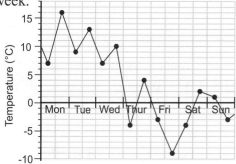

23. The instructions on the bottle of lemon squash are to dilute one measure of squash with five measures of water. Nico pours squash into the measuring jug, as shown in the diagram, and then adds the correct amount of water.

How much squash does he make?

A 0.6 litres   **C** 9 litres   **E** 600 litres
B 0.9 litres   **D** 900 litres

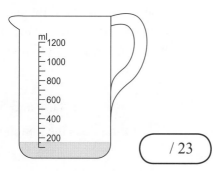

/ 23

Assessment Test 2

Assessment Test 3

Allow 9 minutes to do Section A and 20 minutes to do Section B.
Work as quickly and as carefully as you can.

You can print **multiple-choice answer sheets** for these questions from our website — go to www.cgplearning.co.uk/11+. If you'd prefer to answer them in write-in format, either write your answers in the spaces provided or circle the **correct answer** from the options given.

Section A — Quick Maths
You have **9 minutes** to complete this section.
There are **25 questions** in this section.

1. What is the smallest number that can be made by writing the digits 5, 9 and 0 in these boxes?

2. The tally chart shows the points awarded to four teams in a quiz.

   How many points did Team 4 get?

Team	Number of Points
1	⦀⦀⦀ ‖
2	⦀⦀⦀⦀⦀⦀⦀ ‖‖
3	⦀⦀⦀
4	⦀⦀⦀⦀⦀ ‖‖

3. Competitors ran the following times in a 200 m race.
   25 s, 32 s, 28 s, 36 s, 29 s

   What was the range of times?   seconds

4. The 11 digits in Shazim's telephone number add up to 40. The last two digits add up to 10.
   Some of the digits in Shazim's telephone number are shown on the right.
   What are the two missing digits?

   07700 900_2_

   A   5 and 6   **B**   4 and 7   **C**   7 and 8   **D**   3 and 8   **E**   2 and 8

5. A school canteen is in the shape of regular hexagon and has a perimeter of 78 m.

   What is the length of one side?   metres

6. Tom draws the pentagon shown on the right. Which angle is a reflex angle?
   A   **B**   **C**   **D**   **E**

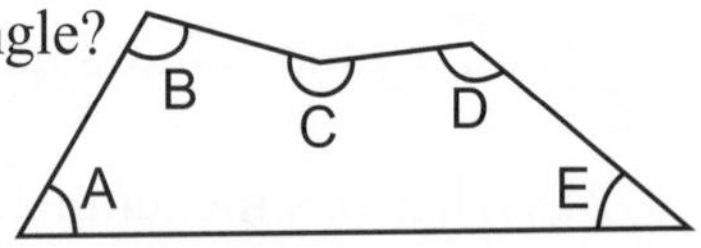

7. What is the best estimate for the length of a double decker bus?
   A   100 mm   **B**   100 cm   **C**   10 m   **D**   100 m   **E**   1 km

8. Sean can fold one paper aeroplane every 20 seconds. How many can he fold in an hour?
   A   60   **B**   30   **C**   1800   **D**   3600   **E**   180

9. The graph on the right shows a family's journey through three towns. How far did they travel between Town B and Town C?   miles

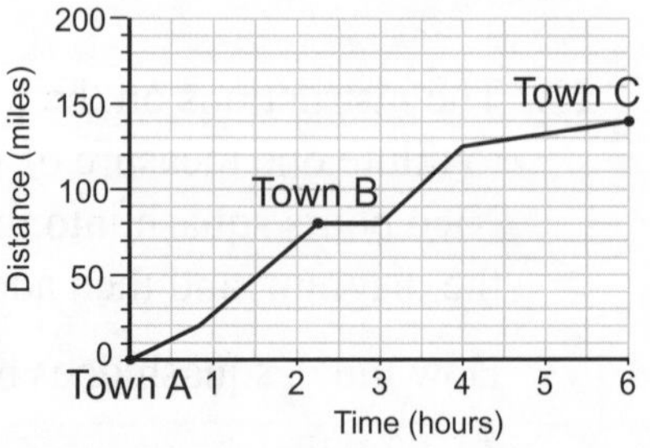

10. A tennis match starts at 3:55 and lasts for three and a half hours.
    What time does the match finish?

Carry on to the next question → →

11. Victor uses white and black squares to make this pattern.

    How many black squares will he need to make the next shape in the pattern?

12. Zuzanna drew this semi-circle on a grid. Each square on the grid is 1 cm².

    Which of the following is the best estimate for the area of the semi-circle?

    A 30 cm²   **C** 40 cm²   **E** 35 cm²
    B 20 cm²   **D** 10 cm²

    1 cm

13. $930 \div 5 = 186$ What is $310 \div 5$?

14. The pictogram on the right shows the colour of every car that passed a school in 1 hour.
    What was the modal colour?

    A Red   **C** Silver   **E** White
    B Black   **D** Blue

Colour	Number of Cars
Red	
Black	
Silver	
Blue	
White	

    = 10 cars

15. A computer screen was left on for 6 hours of the day.

    What percentage of the day is this?   %

16. Kevin finished second in a 400 m race with a time of 61.55 seconds.

    Which of these times could be the winner's time?

    A 61.95   **B** 61.559   **C** 61.543   **D** 61.6   **E** 61.551

17. A school of 709 pupils is divided into teams of 25. How many pupils are left over?
    A 21   **B** 11   **C** 9   **D** 1   **E** 3

18. Yohan draws 5 nets. Which net won't fold up into a cuboid?

    A   **B**   **C**   **D**   **E**

19. Amy writes down the following sequence: 2.25, 1.75, 1.25, 0.75 ...

    What is the next number in this sequence?

20. A box contains chocolate bars with a total weight of 1.4 kg. Each bar of chocolate weighs 70 g.

    How many chocolate bars are there in the box?

Carry on to the next question → →

58

21. A leaking pipe drips once every 12 seconds. It takes 3 hours for the water to fill a 12 litre bowl.
How much water is lost from the pipe in one day? ☐☐☐ litres

22. This list shows the number of words in some maths questions: 27, 33, 38, 26
What is the mean number of words in a question? ☐☐

23. The diagram shows the pattern of floor tiles in Andy's kitchen.
What fraction of the floor tiles are grey? 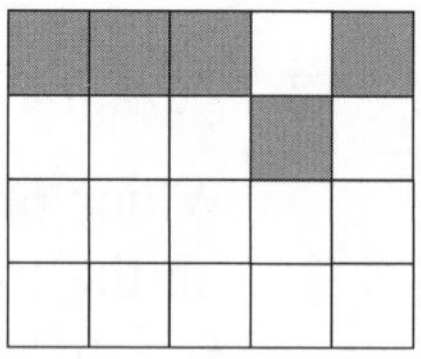
A ⅝   B ¼   C ⁴⁄₂₀   D ³⁄₈   E ⁵⁄₁₀   F ⁵⁄₁₅

24. Luke is thinking of a number. He gives these clues about his number:
    1. It is a multiple of 3.   2. It is a factor of 90.
Which of the following could be Luke's number?
A 24   B 16   C 4   D 30   E 10

25. A fridge uses 0.6 units of electricity each hour.
How much electricity will it use if it is switched on for 150 hours? ☐☐☐ units

/ 25

Section B — Long Maths
You have **20 minutes** to complete this section.
There are **23 questions** in this section.

The board on the right shows the prices of groceries at the Farm Shop.

1. Kelly buys six eggs, two bottles of milk and one packet of cheese from the Farm Shop.
What is the total cost? £ ☐☐.☐☐

2. How much change will Kelly get if she pays with a £20 note? £ ☐☐.☐☐

Farm Shop
Eggs   6 for £1
Rolls   69p each
Milk   99p
Cheese £2.29

3. Jake also has £20. He buys 10 rolls and spends the rest on cheese.
How many packets of cheese can Jake get? ☐

4. The clock on the right shows the time five past twelve.
Between this time and twenty-five past twelve, what angle will the minute hand turn through? ☐☐☐°

A return bus ticket to the museum costs 25p for a child and 99p for an adult.
32 children are going to the museum with 8 teachers.

5. What is the total cost of the bus fares? £ ☐☐.☐☐

6. What percentage of the people going to the museum are teachers? ☐☐ %

Carry on to the next question → →

Assessment Test 3

Barrelburn candles burn down by 2 cm every 13 minutes.

7. How many minutes will a 30 cm Barrelburn candle burn for?

    A 260 minutes   **C** 200 minutes   **E** 780 minutes
    B 195 minutes   **D** 300 minutes

8. Bob bought a Barrelburn candle which took
    2 hours and 10 minutes to burn down completely.
    What was the length of the candle?  cm

9. Megan places two dice on top of each other on a table as shown.
    The number of dots on the opposite faces of each dice add up to 7.
    She can see eight side faces and the face on the top.
    Megan counts all of the dots on the faces she can see.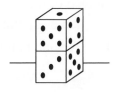

    How many dots does she count?

10. This path is made of circular paving stones which are all
    the same size. ⅓ of some of the paving stones are grey.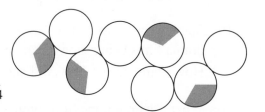

    What fraction of the path is grey?

    A ⅓   **B** ²⁄₄   **C** ²⁄₁₀   **D** ⅙   **E** ¼

11. A packet of sweets contains 4 orange sweets and 3 green sweets. Jane wants to decorate a cake.
    She wants to use a green sweet first and then alternate the colours until she has used 20 sweets.

    How many packets of sweets does she need to buy?

The pie chart on the right shows the proportion of children
wearing hats, scarves and gloves to school.

12. Approximately what percentage of children are wearing gloves?

    A 50%   **B** 60%   **C** 30%   **D** 90%   **E** 75%

13. 20 children were wearing a hat and scarf only.
    How many children are represented in the pie chart?

14. The rectangular faces of this octagonal prism each have an
    area of R and the octagonal faces each have an area of C.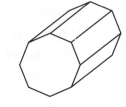

    Which expression shows the total area of all the faces of this octagonal prism?

    A 4R + 4C   **C** 6R + 2C   **E** 2R + 6C
    B 8R + 2C   **D** R + C

Carry on to the next question →→

15. Shannon and Ray measure the perimeter of a rectangular field. The tape measure they use is 27 m long. Along the length of the field, the tape measure fits four times. Along the width of the field, the tape measure fits twice.

What is the perimeter of the field? ☐☐☐ metres

Abraham spins the spinner on the right.

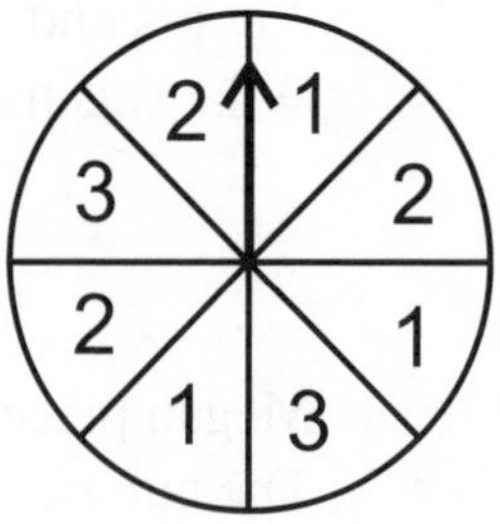

16. What is the probability of spinning a 3? Give your answer as a decimal. ☐.☐☐☐

17. Which of these results is most likely?
    A   An even number   C   A number greater than 1   E   A two
    B   An odd number   D   A number less than 3

The table shows the films shown by a cinema in a year.

18. How many more comedy films than action films are shown? ☐☐

19. Steph went to see 15% of all the drama films being shown that year. How many drama films did she see? ☐☐

| Rating | Type of Film | | |
	Comedy	Drama	Action
U	15	12	7
PG	11	15	8
12A	14	24	4
15	18	29	4

20. What fraction of the films with a 12A rating were comedy?

    A $\frac{1}{3}$ B $\frac{14}{40}$ C $\frac{6}{24}$ D $\frac{3}{8}$ E $\frac{7}{18}$

21. Kris draws the Venn diagram on the right. How many numbers between 1 and 100 would go into the shaded area of the Venn diagram? ☐☐

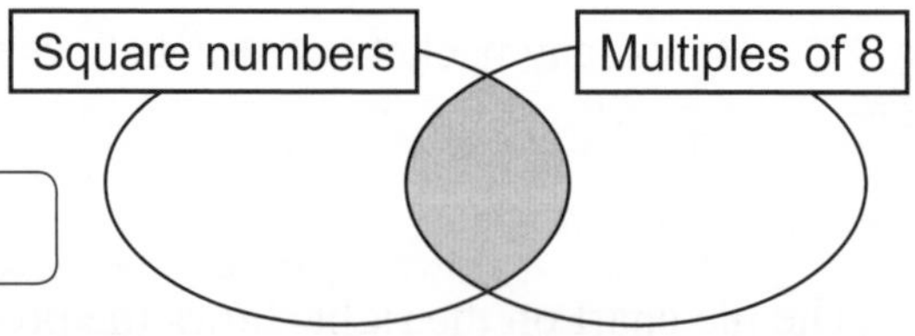

Square numbers   Multiples of 8

Mirror line

Stuart draws a triangle on this coordinate grid.

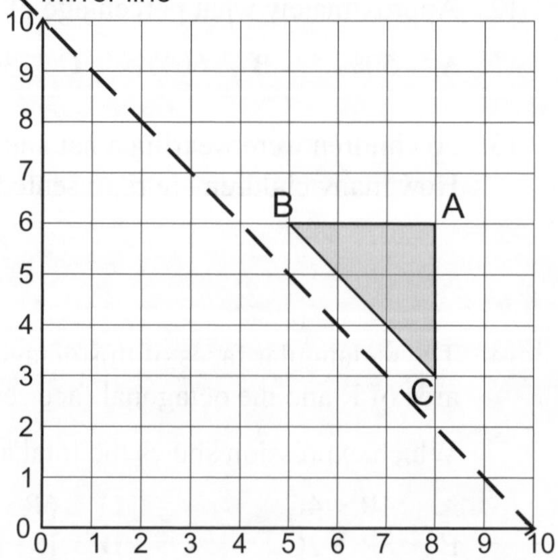

22. He rotates the triangle 180° clockwise about corner B.

    What are the new coordinates of corner C after the rotation? (☐,☐)

23. He reflects his original triangle in the mirror line.

    What are the coordinates of the image of corner A after the reflection? (☐,☐)

/ 23

Assessment Test 3

Assessment Test 4

Allow 9 minutes to do Section A and 20 minutes to do Section B.
Work as quickly and as carefully as you can.

You can print **multiple-choice answer sheets** for these questions from our website — go to
www.cgplearning.co.uk/11+. If you'd prefer to answer them in write-in format, either write
your answers in the spaces provided or circle the **correct answer** from the options given.

Section A — Quick Maths
You have **9 minutes** to complete this section.
There are **25 questions** in this section.

---

1. Which of these is the smallest number?

    A 0.57   **B** 16.01   **C** 1.63   **D** 0.23   **E** 8.1

2. The table on the right shows when five children were born.
    Who is the youngest?

    A Archie   **C** Sara   **E** Mena
    B Damien   **D** Hamid

	Month	Year
Archie	June	1999
Damien	January	1999
Sara	May	1997
Hamid	December	1999
Mena	February	1997

3. A full jug holds 2.5 litres of water.
    How many 250 ml glasses could a full jug fill?

4. Rearrange the digits in 27 149 to make
    the largest even number possible.

5. How many millimetres are there in 3.5 metres?

    A 35   **B** 350   **C** 3050   **D** 3500   **E** 35 000

6. The shape on the right is reflected in a mirror line.

    What new shape will be made?

    A rectangle   **C** pentagon   **E** hexagon
    B quadrilateral   **D** rhombus

    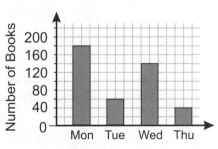

7. Liam divides a number by 5. He is left with a remainder of 3.
    Which of the following could have been his original number?

    A 42   **B** 17   **C** 23   **D** 9   **E** 21

8. The graph shows the number of books borrowed
    from the school library over four days.

    What was the total number of books
    borrowed on Wednesday and Thursday?

9. How many weeks after the
    19th January is the 23rd February?   weeks

Carry on to the next question →→
Assessment Test 4

10. In a sale a dress is reduced by 25%.
    The original price was £16. What is the sale price?   £ ☐☐.☐☐

11. Salma buys a bag of apples for £2.50.
    There are 10 apples in the bag. How much does each apple cost?   ☐☐☐ p

12. Look at the shape on the right. Which two lines are perpendicular?
    A   N and O   C   N and R   E   Q and P
    B   Q and R   D   O and Q

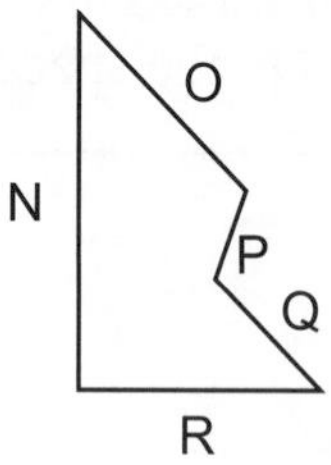

13. Maddy starts at 10 and counts back in steps of $1\frac{1}{2}$.
    Which of these numbers will she count?
    A   6   B   5   C   4   D   3   E   2

14. Look at the shape on the right. Estimate the size of angle y.
    A   45°   B   90°   C   75°   D   20°   E   10°

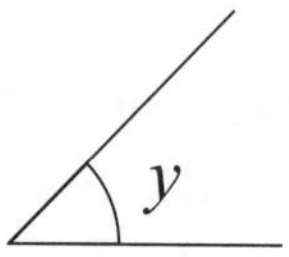

15. The temperature in Hameed's garden is –3 °C. The temperature in Hameed's kitchen is 21 °C.
    What is the difference between the two temperatures?   ☐☐ °C

16. Which of these is the best estimate for the weight of a guinea pig?
    A   17.5 g   B   750 g   C   75 kg   D   7 g   E   700 kg

17. [234 ÷ 9 = 26]   What is 468 ÷ 9?   ☐☐

18. What is the size of angle h?   ☐☐ °

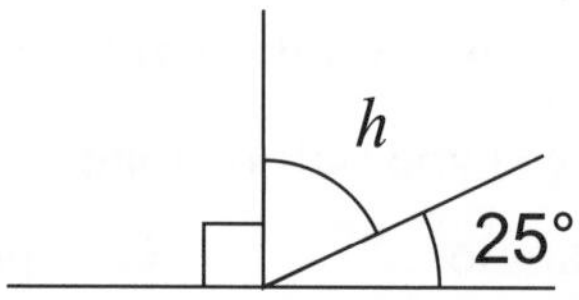

19. Which set of numbers has the greatest mode?
    A   3, 7, 7, 8, 9   B   8, 4, 9, 6, 4   C   2, 5, 2, 1, 6   D   6, 6, 8, 7, 9   E   7, 5, 8, 5, 3

20. A recipe to make 10 pies requires 200 g of flour.
    How much flour would be needed to make 15 pies?   ☐☐☐ g

21. The diagram shows a weighing scale.
    What weight, in kilograms, will the scale show
    if the pointer rotates 270° clockwise?   ☐☐ kg

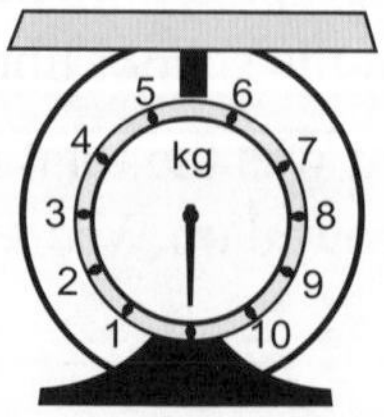

22. What is 20.7 × 6?
    A   138.6   B   120.42   C   116.4   D   124.2   E   136.8

Carry on to the next question →→

23. The diagram shows a rectangular school playground.
Chris ran around the perimeter of the playground twice.

How many metres did Chris run? ⬚⬚⬚ m

7 m | Playground
18 m

24. How many fifths are there in 5?

A 25   B 5   C 1   D 21   E 17

25. Which of the following points is not inside the shaded circle?

A (8, 4)   C (2, 3)   E (5, 3)
B (6, 6)   D (4, 7)

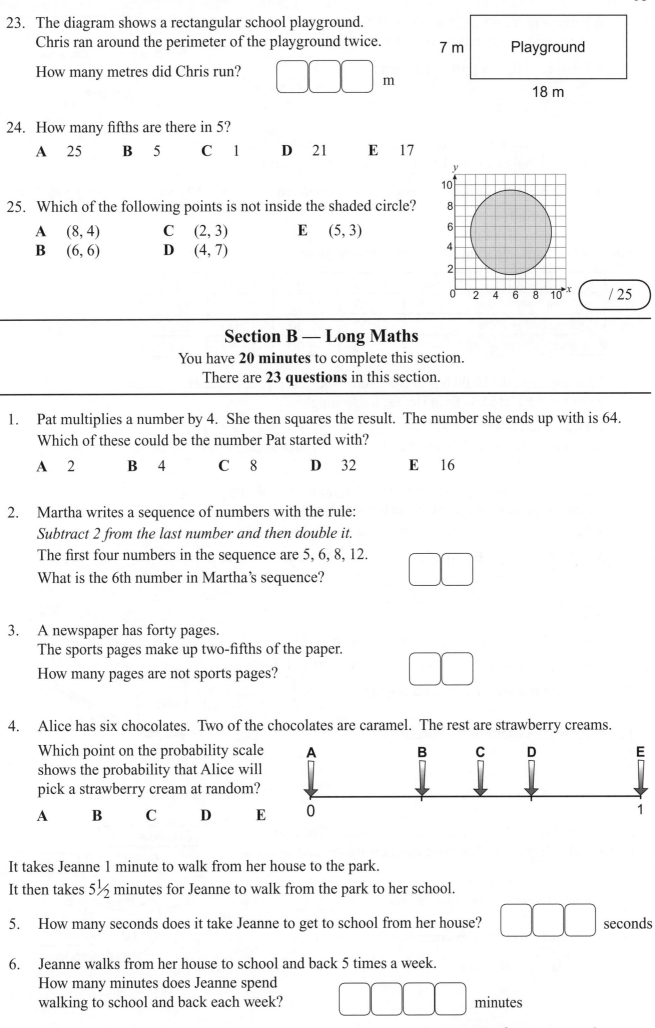

/ 25

Section B — Long Maths

You have **20 minutes** to complete this section.
There are **23 questions** in this section.

---

1. Pat multiplies a number by 4. She then squares the result. The number she ends up with is 64.
Which of these could be the number Pat started with?

A 2   B 4   C 8   D 32   E 16

2. Martha writes a sequence of numbers with the rule:
Subtract 2 from the last number and then double it.
The first four numbers in the sequence are 5, 6, 8, 12.
What is the 6th number in Martha's sequence?   ⬚⬚

3. A newspaper has forty pages.
The sports pages make up two-fifths of the paper.

How many pages are not sports pages?   ⬚⬚

4. Alice has six chocolates. Two of the chocolates are caramel. The rest are strawberry creams.

Which point on the probability scale
shows the probability that Alice will
pick a strawberry cream at random?

A B C D E

A   B   C   D   E
0   1

It takes Jeanne 1 minute to walk from her house to the park.
It then takes $5\frac{1}{2}$ minutes for Jeanne to walk from the park to her school.

5. How many seconds does it take Jeanne to get to school from her house?   ⬚⬚⬚ seconds

6. Jeanne walks from her house to school and back 5 times a week.
How many minutes does Jeanne spend
walking to school and back each week?   ⬚⬚⬚ minutes

Carry on to the next question →→
Assessment Test 4

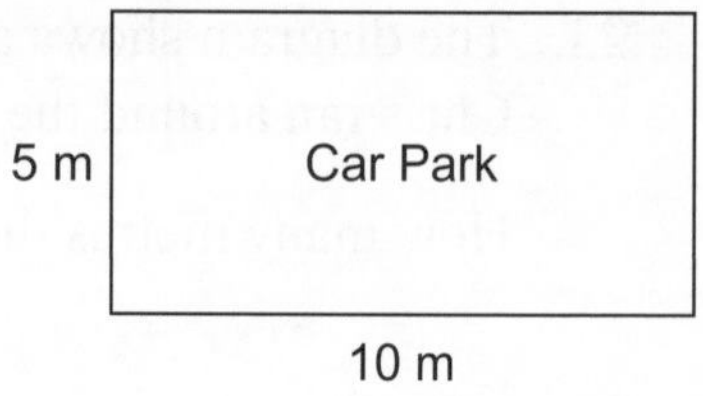

7. A parking space for a car needs to be 5 m long and 3 m wide.
The car park on the right is used for three spaces.

What area of the car park is left over? ⬚⬚ m²

5 m | Car Park

10 m

8. The circumference of a wheel is 85.5 cm. It is rolled along a corridor.
The wheel makes 7 complete turns. How far does it roll?

A 585.5 cm   **B** 590 cm   **C** 558 cm   **D** 625.5 cm   **E** 598.5 cm

This is a bus timetable from Blackford to Birmingham.

Blackford	10:00	10:30	11:00	11:30	12:00
Henley	10:45	11:15	11:45	12:15	12:45
Dunny-on-the-Wold	—	12:00	12:30	13:00	13:30
Birmingham	—	12:30	13:00	13:30	14:00

9. Louise gets on the 10:00 bus at Blackford. She gets off the bus at Henley and waits for the 11:15 bus from Henley to Birmingham.

How long did it take Louise to
get from Blackford to Birmingham? ⬚ hours and ⬚⬚ minutes

10. Ahmed lives in Henley and his home is ten minutes walk from the bus stop. He wants to arrive in Birmingham by 13:15.
What is the latest time that Ahmed should leave his home?

A 11:45   **B** 11:15   **C** 11:35   **D** 12:05   **E** 10:45

The wooden block shown on the right is a cuboid.

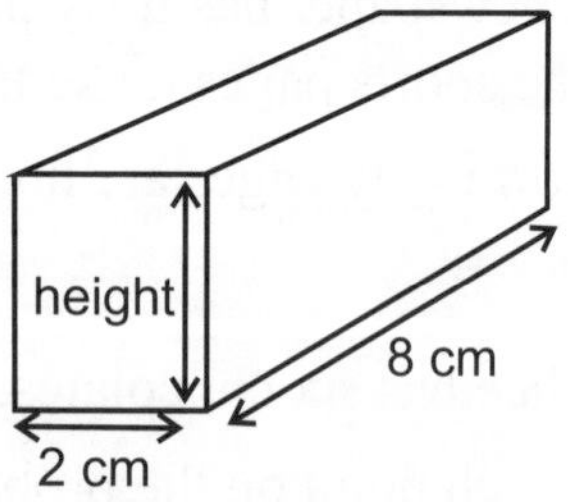

11. The width and height of the cuboid are in the ratio 1:3.

The width is 2 cm. What is the height? ⬚⬚ cm

12. What is the volume of the cuboid? ⬚⬚ cm³

height | 8 cm | 2 cm

Daud asked the children in his class whether they like Chinese, Indian and Italian food. The Venn diagram shows their answers.

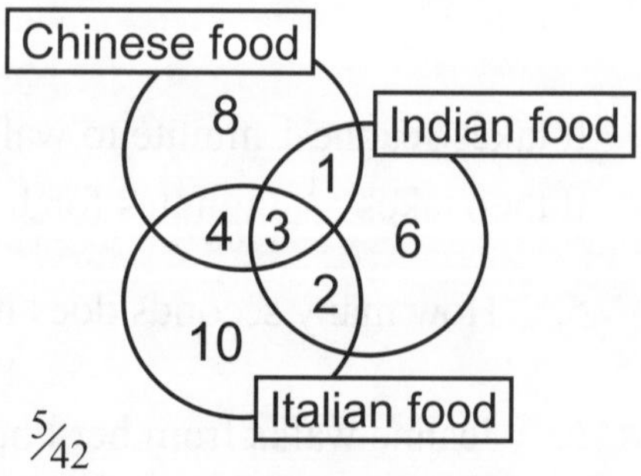

13. How many children in total like
Chinese food or Italian food or both? ⬚⬚

14. What fraction of the class only like Italian food?

A ¹⁹⁄₃₄   **B** ⁵⁄₁₇   **C** ¹²⁄₃₄   **D** ⁹⁄₁₇   **E** ⁵⁄₄₂

Chinese food | 8 | Indian food | 1 | 4 3 | 6 | 2 | 10 | Italian food

Carry on to the next question →→

15. Magdalena buys two dresses. One costs £X and the other costs £Y.
    She also buys three blouses which each cost £Z.

    Which expression shows the total amount that she spends in pounds?

    A $X + Y + 3Z$ **C** $3Z$ **E** $2X + 2Y + 3Z$

    B $X + Y + Z$ **D** $X + Y$

Some people were asked where they went on holiday. The results were recorded in a pie chart.

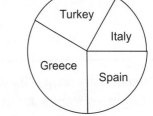

16. What percentage of people
    either went to Greece or Italy?   %

17. 12 people went to Turkey.
    How many people did not go to Turkey?

The colours of the front doors of houses in
a street were recorded in a pictogram.

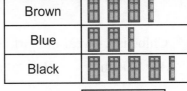

18. How many more black doors
    were there than blue ones?

19. What was the ratio of brown doors to blue doors?
    Give your answer in its simplest form.

The table shows the number of goals scored by the teams taking part in a netball tournament.

20. What percentage of the teams
    scored more than two goals?   %

Number of goals	1	2	3	4	5
Number of teams	3	3	1	2	1

21. What fraction of teams scored less than three goals?

    A $\frac{3}{10}$ **B** $\frac{2}{5}$ **C** $\frac{5}{10}$ **D** $\frac{3}{5}$ **E** $\frac{7}{10}$

22. Manjit buys six cartons of apple juice. She pays
    with a ten pound note and receives £2.80 in change.

    How much does each carton of apple juice cost? £

23. The bar chart shows the number of lengths of a
    swimming pool that some of the children in a class swam.

    How many children did not swim if there are 30 children
    in the class altogether?

    A 9   **C** 29   **E** 12

    B 1   **D** 5

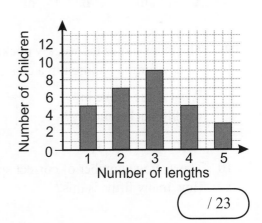

/ 23

Assessment Test 4

Assessment Test 5

Allow 9 minutes to do Section A and 20 minutes to do Section B.
Work as quickly and as carefully as you can.

You can print **multiple-choice answer sheets** for these questions from our website — go to
www.cgplearning.co.uk/11+. If you'd prefer to answer them in write-in format, either write
your answers in the spaces provided or circle the **correct answer** from the options given.

Section A — Quick Maths
You have **9 minutes** to complete this section.
There are **25 questions** in this section.

1. A stationery shop sells staples in boxes of 3000.
   How many staples are in five boxes? staples

2. Topi has 136 DVDs. She can fit fifty DVDs on each shelf.
   How many shelves does Topi need to store all the DVDs? shelves

3. Chloe is a 4-year-old girl. Which of these is most likely to be her height?
   A   40 cm   **B**   80 mm   **C**   0.5 km   **D**   2 m   **E**   90 cm

4. $56 \times 946 = 52\,976$ What is 946×28?

5. There are 25 pencils in a box. A box of pencils costs £4.99.
   How much does it cost to buy 75 pencils? £

6. A school is planning to build a small swimming pool.
   Which unit would be best to use to measure the volume of water needed to fill the pool?
   A   kg   **B**   km^3 **C**   m   **D**   m^3 **E**   ml

7. Joe has a piece of wood that is 99 cm long. He removes 1.8 mm using a sanding machine.
   What is the length, in centimetres, of the sanded piece of wood? cm

8. The height of five newly planted trees was measured in metres. Which tree was the smallest?
   A $1\frac{1}{5}$ m   **B** $1\frac{1}{4}$ m   **C**   1.05 m   **D**   1.5 m   **E**   1.25 m

9. The table shows the weekly pocket
   money for the children in a class.

   What is the range in
   weekly pocket money?   £

Weekly pocket money	Number of children
50p	3
£1.00	8
£1.50	7
£2.00	6
£2.50	4

10. The average number of correct spellings on a spelling test was 6.4.
    How many fifths is this?

Carry on to the next question →→

11. George shades in part of this rectangle. What fraction has he shaded?

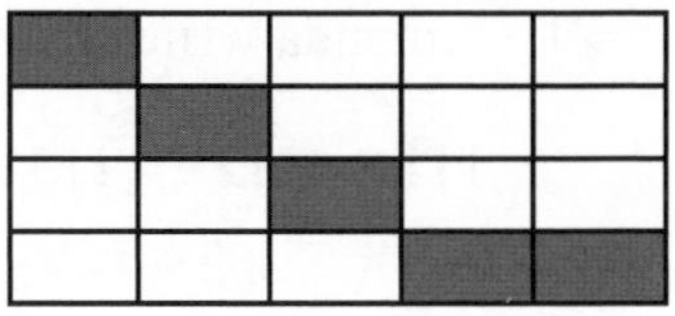

    A ⅔   B ⅕   C ¼   D ½   E ⅓

12. Look at the diagram. Which of the following describes the route from the supermarket to the chemist?

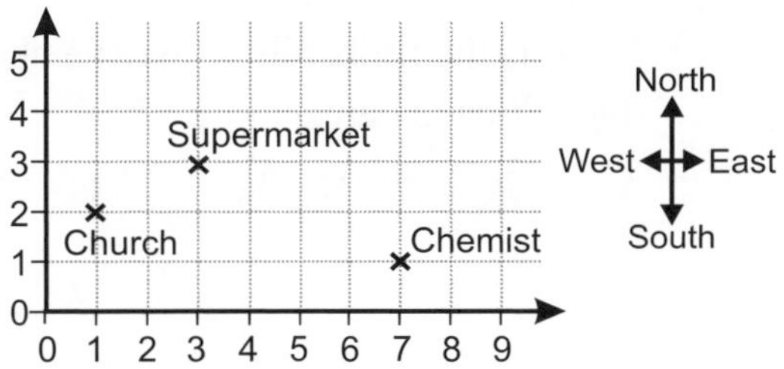

    A   4 squares west, 2 squares north
    B   2 squares west, 1 square south
    C   3 squares south, 1 square east
    D   4 squares east, 2 squares south
    E   2 squares south, 4 squares west

13. Halima counts backwards from 39 in steps of 9. Which of these numbers will she count?

    A 7   B 6   C 5   D 4   E 3

14. The diagram shows a triangle. Two of the angles in the triangle are given.
    What is the size of the third angle? ☐☐☐ °

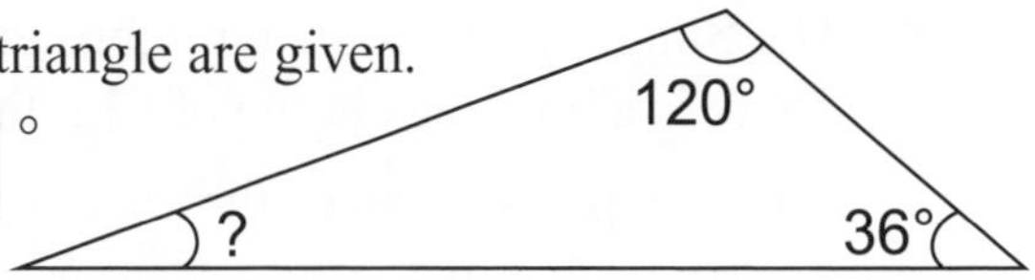

15. Rearrange the digits in 94 411 to make the smallest odd number possible. ☐☐☐☐☐

16. The table shows some information given on the label on a tin of baked beans.

    How many grams of carbohydrate would a 1 kg tin of baked beans contain? ☐☐☐ g

	Typical values per 100 g
Protein	4.4 g
Fat	0.6 g
Carbohydrate	13.4 g
Fibre	4.2 g

17. The grid on the right shows the shape of a wheat field with corners at A, B and C.
    What are the coordinates of corner C? (☐ , ☐)

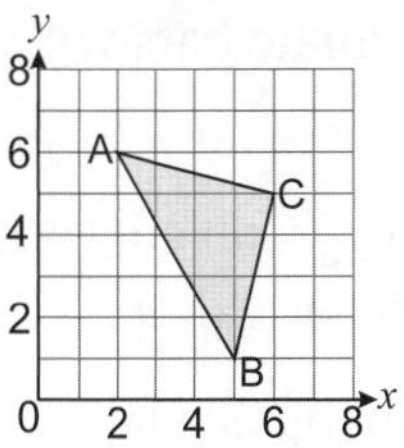

18. Helena is 5^2 years old and her aunty is twice her age.
    How old is her aunty? ☐☐ years old

19. The average yearly temperature on the south coast of England was rounded up to 11.45 °C.
    Which of these numbers could be the actual average?

    A   11.458 °C   B   11.426 °C   C   11.46°C   D   11.4501 °C   E   11.451 °C

20. A coach departs at 8:50 and takes 2 hours and 25 minutes to get to its destination. What time does it arrive? ☐☐:☐☐

Carry on to the next question →→
Assessment Test 5

21. Amanda writes the following sequence. What number should come next?

    111   112   115   120   127   ⬜⬜⬜

22. The diagram shows part of a juice bar menu.
    Shahida chooses a drink from the menu at random.

    What is the probability that she chooses a drink that
    doesn't have banana in it?

    A $\frac{2}{5}$ B $\frac{3}{5}$ C $\frac{2}{11}$ D $\frac{1}{5}$ E $\frac{3}{7}$

MENU	
Drink	Contains
Pink Fizz	Raspberry, Banana
Lemon Zing	Lemon, Orange
Fairy Drink	Orange, Kiwi
Redberry punch	Strawberry, Banana
Apple Fizz	Apple, Orange

23. Which numbers on this diagram are multiples of both 3 and 5?

    A   42, 75, 135   C   42, 75   E   75, 135
    B   135, 42   D   25, 75, 135

    25   42   64
      135   75   28

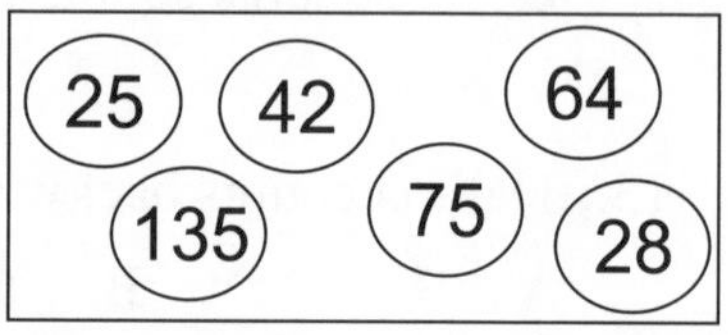

24. The Singh family book a minibus to the airport.
    There is a booking charge of £12, then a charge of £2 per mile.

    Which expression gives the cost in pounds for a journey that is y miles long?

    A $12y$ B $12y + 2$ C $14y + 12$ D $14 + 2y$ E $12 + 2y$

25. The diagram shows a dial on a weighing scale.
    What weight does the pointer show?   ⬜.⬜⬜ kg

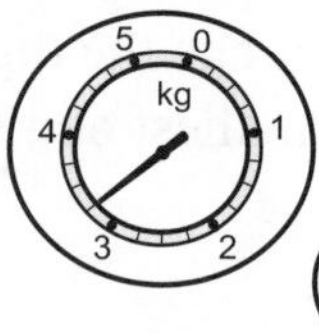

    / 25

Section B — Long Maths

You have **20 minutes** to complete this section.
There are **23 questions** in this section.

1. Lucy buys four friends a chocolate bar each. Each bar costs 89p.
   How much change will she get if she pays for
   the chocolate bars with a five pound note?   £ ⬜.⬜⬜

2. This line graph converts fuel consumption in km per litre
   to miles per gallon.

   Mr Khan buys a new car with a fuel
   consumption of 15 km per litre.

   How many miles per gallon is this?   ⬜⬜ miles/gallon

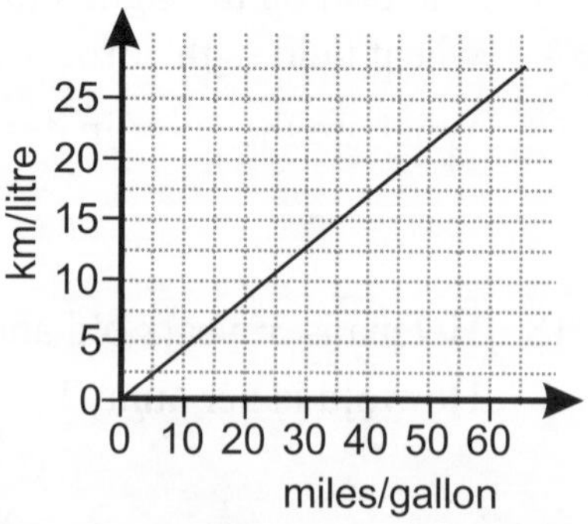

3. Which of the following shapes should be put in the shaded box
   of the sorting table?

   A   square   D   rectangle
   B   right-angled triangle E   parallelogram
   C   equilateral triangle

	At least 2 equal sides	No equal sides
At least 1 obtuse angle		
No obtuse angles		

Carry on to the next question →→

The diagram shows a set of steps. All the steps are the same size.

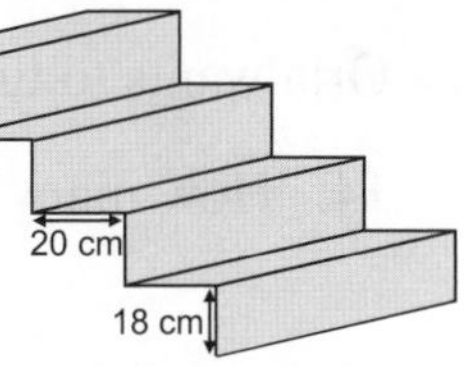

4. What length of carpet is needed to cover all the steps without any left over?

   A   180 cm   **B**   152 cm   **C**   160 cm   **D**   142 cm   **E**   148 cm

   20 cm

   18 cm

5. If each step is 2 m wide, what area of carpet is needed (in m²)?

   ☐☐.☐☐☐ m²

6. Andrew sells scones for £1 each on his stall at the market. It costs him 52p to make each scone. How much profit does he make if he sells 80 scones?

   £☐☐.☐☐

The pie chart shows how Sunita spends the 24 hours of Saturday.

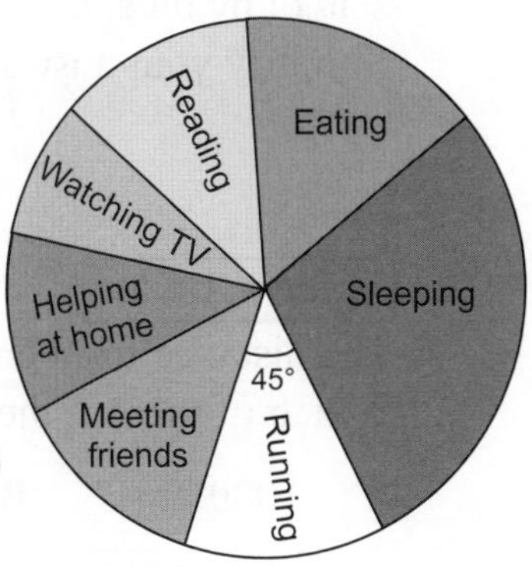

7. How many hours does Sunita spend running?

   A   2   **B**   4   **C**   3   **D**   5   **E**   6

8. On Saturday Sunita runs for an hour more than she watches TV. What proportion of the 24 hours of Saturday did she spend watching TV? Simplify your answer.

   ☐ in every ☐☐ hours

9. Sunita spent 7 hours sleeping on Saturday and 9 hours sleeping on Sunday. What fraction of the 48 hours did she spend sleeping?

   A $^{16}/_{24}$ **B** $^{6}/_{12}$ **C** $^{1}/_{3}$ **D** $^{4}/_{6}$ **E** $^{3}/_{8}$

Each of the 5 members of the Brown family take two chicken sandwiches for lunch on 5 days of the week.

10. Each sandwich contains 40 g of chicken. If 1 kg of chicken costs £6.49, how much will they spend on chicken for their sandwiches each week?

    £☐☐.☐☐

11. Each chicken sandwich takes 2 slices of bread. There are 20 slices of bread in a loaf. How many loaves of bread do the Brown family use for their sandwiches in a year (52 weeks)?

    ☐☐☐☐

12. Hayley counts the number of cars of different colours in the school car park. She works out that 5% of the cars are red.

    If there are 3 red cars, how many cars are there, in total, in the car park?

    ☐☐

13. Aran spins the spinner on the right. Which of the following statements is true?

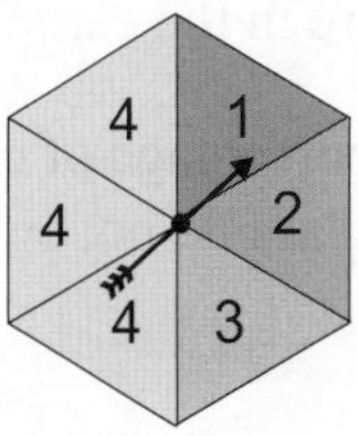

    A   You are less likely to spin a 4 than a 1.
    B   You are less likely to spin an odd number than a 2.
    C   You are more likely to spin an even number than an odd number.
    D   You are certain to spin a number less than 4.
    E   You have an even chance of spinning a number greater than 2.

Carry on to the next question →→

Assessment Test 5

Orla wants to turf her garden. A roll of turf is 4 m long and 1 m wide.

14. How many rolls of turf does Orla need to buy?

15. A roll of turf costs £10.50.
How much will it cost Orla to turf her garden? £ ☐☐☐.☐☐

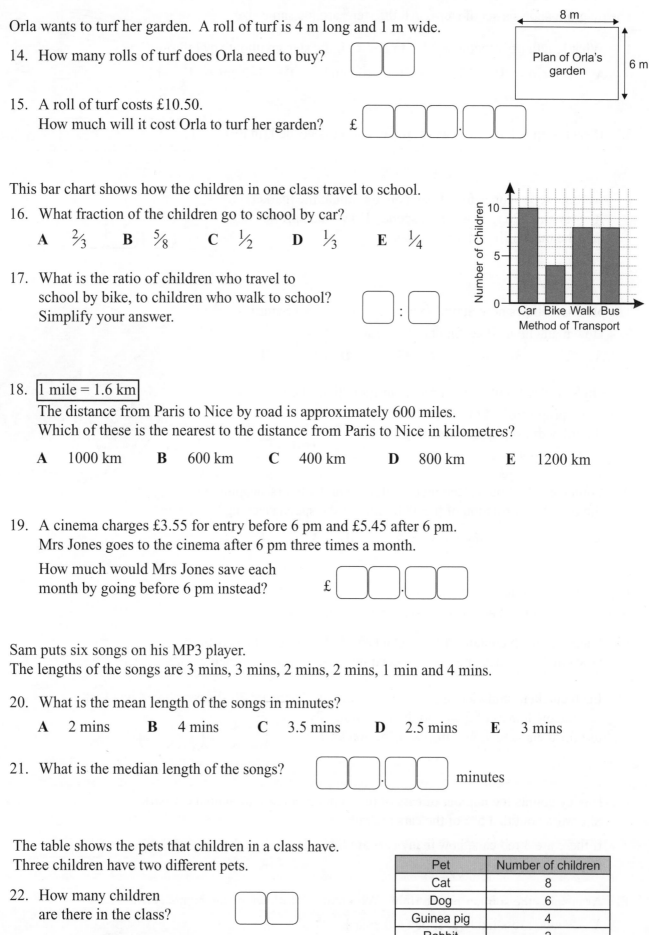

Plan of Orla's garden — 8 m × 6 m

This bar chart shows how the children in one class travel to school.

16. What fraction of the children go to school by car?

A ⅔ B ⅝ C ½ D ⅓ E ¼

17. What is the ratio of children who travel to school by bike, to children who walk to school? Simplify your answer.

☐ : ☐

18. | 1 mile = 1.6 km |

The distance from Paris to Nice by road is approximately 600 miles.
Which of these is the nearest to the distance from Paris to Nice in kilometres?

A 1000 km B 600 km C 400 km D 800 km E 1200 km

19. A cinema charges £3.55 for entry before 6 pm and £5.45 after 6 pm.
Mrs Jones goes to the cinema after 6 pm three times a month.

How much would Mrs Jones save each month by going before 6 pm instead? £ ☐☐.☐☐

Sam puts six songs on his MP3 player.
The lengths of the songs are 3 mins, 3 mins, 2 mins, 2 mins, 1 min and 4 mins.

20. What is the mean length of the songs in minutes?

A 2 mins B 4 mins C 3.5 mins D 2.5 mins E 3 mins

21. What is the median length of the songs? ☐☐.☐☐ minutes

The table shows the pets that children in a class have.
Three children have two different pets.

22. How many children are there in the class?

23. What percentage of children in the class do not own a pet? ☐☐ %

Pet	Number of children
Cat	8
Dog	6
Guinea pig	4
Rabbit	2
Mouse	1
None	12

/ 23

Assessment Test 5